The Glass Slipper

The Glass Slipper

ELEANOR FARJEON

HarperTrophy
A Division of HarperCollinsPublishers

Library of Congress Cataloging-in-Publication Data
Farjeon, Eleanor, 1881–1965
    The glass slipper.

    Summary: In her haste to flee the palace before the
fairy godmother's magic loses effect, Cinderella leaves
behind a glass slipper.
    [1. Fairy tales.   2. Folklore—France]   I. Cinderella.
II. Title.
PZ8.F233G1   1986   [398.2]   85-45853
ISBN 0-397-32180-5
ISBN 0-397-32181-3 (lib. bdg.)
ISBN 0-06-440561-3 (pbk.)

First Harper Trophy edition, 1995.

Contents

The
Glass Slipper

CHAPTER I

The Things in the Kitchen

OUTSIDE THE KITCHEN, in the falling snow, the Rooster crowed: *"Cockadoodledoo!"*

Inside the kitchen, in her narrow bed, Ella pulled the thin blanket over her ears and tried not to hear him. As well as being thin, the blanket was short, so when she covered her head it left her little feet bare. They were not only the prettiest, but the littlest pair of feet that any girl of sixteen was ever blessed with; but when they poked out of the blanket they were blue with cold.

The kitchen was a vast, dark, stony room, more like a cellar than a kitchen, which is often the coziest room in a house; but nothing could make this cold vault cozy, even when the fire was lit on the wide, open hearth. The room had barred windows with wooden shutters, and a heavy door with iron bolts that opened onto the coaching road. On the left the road ran to the city, and on the right to the King's palace, and beyond it stretched the forest, green in summer, yellow in autumn, white in winter.

"Cockadoodledoo!" crowed the Rooster in the snow.

"Silly old Rooster!" muttered Ella in her bed— if you could call it a bed. Ella did, because it was the only one she had. When she was a little girl, she had slept in a lovely room upstairs. She buried her face in her pillow and began to think about a long time ago, when she had a little gilt bed with soft blankets and a blue silk coverlet, which her mother tucked in when she came to kiss Ella good night. She remembered a lovely party, full of fun and dancing, and a game of hide-and-seek. Children ran here and there, calling, *"Where are you?"* She wore a lovely party frock, like a rainbow.

As she lay thinking, she clasped her one treasure left over from the happy time, a miniature of that pretty young Mother with fair hair, and blue eyes smiling out of her roseleaf face. Ella kept this picture hidden under her pillow, where nobody knew about it. . . . Her thinking changed to the time, after her Mother died, when her Father took another wife who already had two daughters of her own. These three ladies now had the grandest rooms upstairs for themselves, and Ella was sent down to the basement to sleep as well as to live. "And count yourself lucky!" said her Stepmother. "It isn't every growing girl who has a bed-sitting room of her own." Well, there *was* a creaky rocking chair to sit on, and a box-bed in the wall to sleep in. When you were right inside the bed, it could be shut from outside with a long sliding shutter. Sometimes, in one of her nastiest tempers, the Stepmother shut Ella in and fastened the shutter with a metal bar, and Ella had to lie in the dark till the Stepmother stopped being in the temper. However, besides having the prettiest little feet and the most charming little face in the kingdom, Ella had also the sweetest and sunniest disposition. She made the best of everything when she could, and when she couldn't she gulped down her tears, gave herself a shake, and went on again. It wasn't always easy, but she managed it somehow.

"*Cockadoodledoo!*" crowed the Rooster for the third time.

"There you go!" said Ella, sitting up. "'*Time to get up*'—I know! Light the fire—boil the kettle—

fill the lamp—sweep the ashes—lay the table—bake the cake—scrub the step—feed the hens—and especially the silly-shrilly snappy-flappy old cock! *I know.*"

"*Cockadoodledoo!*" crowed the Rooster.

"*Cockadoodledoo!*" mocked Ella. "Well, I won't! Everybody else orders me about, but *you* shan't!" And down she lay with her fingers in her ears. That seemed to finish the Rooster, and he didn't crow again.

But now all round the kitchen went the funny little stir that meant the day had begun and Things weren't being attended to. The tall clock in the corner seemed to be ticking a little more impressively than before, and Ella couldn't shut it out:

"Tick-tock!
Tick-tock!
The Grandfather Clock
Agrees with the Cock."

And as it began to strike seven:

"Bing-Bong!
Bing-Bong!
It's exceedingly wrong
To stay in bed long."

Ella sat up again with a little sigh. "All right, Grandpa. *I* know. You never let me off, do you?"

"I never let anybody off," ticked the Clock.

"I'm just your slave, aren't I?" grumbled Ella. The Clock didn't answer. Ella put one bare foot down on the icy stone floor and drew it back with a shudder. "Br-r-rr! It's colder than ever this morning. Oh dear!"

Over the grimy sink the Tap began to drip:

> "Drip, drop!
> Drip, drop!
> Make haste with the mop,
> The mop and the slop."

There are few things more irritating than a dripping tap, and Ella said rather crossly, "Tap, Tap, why *must* you drip?"

"I like that!" said the Tap. "You left me dripping last night."

"Oh dear!" sighed Ella again. "I wish taps had never been invented."

The Tap didn't answer.

Ella put both feet together on the floor and stood up, fastening her petticoat round her waist. "I wish I had some proper shoes," she said. But she hadn't even a pair of socks for the little cold feet in their ragged sandals, and when she had pulled a cotton frock over her head, her dressing was completed. While she smoothed her hair with her hands, the birch broom in the corner started jigging up and down.

> "Brush, Broom!
> Brush, Broom!
> The grime in the room
> Could do with a groom."

"Broom, Broom!" cried Ella. "Can't you ever rest?"

"You didn't sweep the floor last night," thumped the Broom.

"I know I didn't. I *hate* sweeping the floor."

The Broom didn't answer.

But now the Fire Irons clattered on the hearth, and before they could reprove her, she cried, "Stop clattering, Poker and Tongs! I'll light the fire in a minute." Hardly had she spoken when the Rocking Chair started rocking with a squeak and a creak. "Stop creaking, Chair! I'll oil you in a jiffy," cried Ella.

And now all the Things in the kitchen set to on her at once:

> "Light me!
> Oil me!
> Sweep me!
> Boil me!
> Mend me!
> Make me!
> Clean me!
> Bake me!"

"Stop it!" cried Ella, stamping her foot at them. *"Stop it at once!"*

The dripping and thumping and clatter and creaking stopped on the spot. Ella looked round the room, a little scared by the sudden silence.

"I never did *see* such Things!" she declared. But none of them answered. "Oh dear!" she sighed. "Now they're cross. Oh dear!" She went to the sink, and the pile of yesterday's dirty crockery dismayed her. "Just look at all this washing-up!" She hoped to soften the Things' hearts by making them sorry for her. After all, they were her best friends, except, of course, her father. But he had to go away so often on business that she was sometimes lonely for weeks and weeks on end; and when he *was* at home it wasn't much use, because of the Stepmother's temper and the Stepsisters' domineering ways. Ella picked a tea-stained cup out of the sink and asked reproachfully, "Cup, Cup, how would you like it if you had to wash *me* up?" The Cup didn't answer.

Oh, very well, if they wouldn't be friends they wouldn't! There was always the cat to talk to, and—what luck! There was still a drain of yesterday's milk in the jug. She took it over to the cupboard by the hearth, where Tabitha lay coiled up in the dark, waiting for her new family to arrive.

"Tabby, Tabby, would you like some breakfast?" Ella peered down at the little cat, who lifted the tip of her nose from the tip of her tail, and gave a little *pirrup*. "What, haven't your kittens come *yet*?" Ella poured the milk into a saucer and put it down carefully under the little cat's chin. "Never mind, Tabby, they soon will. Now for the washing-up!"

She left Tabby lapping her breakfast and returned to the sink. "Can't wash up till I boil the kettle." Over to the hearth went she. "Can't boil the kettle till I light the fire." Down on her knees went she. "Fire, Fire, are you going to be cross this morning too? Coal, Coal, I wish you didn't have clinkers. Oh, Wood, I wish you weren't so damp." And while she swept up the ashes and picked out the clinkers and laid the wood crisscross on the fire bricks, Ella went on wishing for the things she wished most.

"I wish plates didn't get greasy. . . . I wish sweeping and scrubbing and scouring did themselves when I wasn't looking. . . . I wish potatoes peeled themselves while my back was turned. . . . I wish bells didn't keep on ringing and ringing and ringing. . . . I wish coal buckets carried themselves to and from the coal cellar. . . . I wish tables didn't want laying, and tableclothes didn't want ironing, and spoons and forks didn't want polishing. I wish people ate out of the dish with their fingers. . . . I wish there was lots more time for having fun. . . . I wish there was somebody to have the fun with. . . . I wish . . . I wish . . . I wish . . ."

The last wish never got itself said. Ella wasn't quite sure what it was. She only knew that it was for something very lovely, after the work was done and even the fun had come to an end.

"I wish . . ."

The Fire gave a great puff of smoke at her as she hung the heavy kettle on its hook. She sat back on her heels, rubbing the smoke out of her eyes. She wished . . . What did she wish?

Outside the door she heard the jingle of harness and the clatter of a horse's hoofs on the snowy road.

CHAPTER II

Ella and Her Father

"FATHER!" cried Ella.

Yes, after being a month away, her Father was home again. Ella would have known Dobbin's hoofs from any others on the road. She ran to the cupboard to share the good news with Tabby. "Father's come home!" Tabitha purred.

Oh, but supposing he was going to ride round to the front of the house? Ella flew to the kitchen door and pulled back the heavy bolts. "Father! Come in this way! Please do—*please*. Do you mind?"

Of course he didn't mind! He was as glad as Ella of this secret chance to have her to himself. It was a thing they didn't exactly speak about, for Ella knew it troubled him, and she tried not to let him know that it troubled her too. Her Father always hoped that his little Ella was happy down in the kitchen by herself, and so, in a way, she was—well, *rather* happy; happier, she sometimes thought, than Father was, living upstairs with the three cross-patches. If only he could have lived down in the kitchen with her, Ella would have been quite happy; as indeed she was now, brushing the snow from his heavy cape. When she helped him off with it he gave her a quick, shy kiss, as if he was afraid somebody might be looking. She returned the kiss, saying cheerfully, "Welcome home, Father. How early you've come back. You must have been riding all night."

"Through the snow too," said her Father, rubbing his cold fingers.

"Have you had any breakfast?"

He confessed that he hadn't.

"Oh, do have it down here!" cried Ella. "I'll get you some—what fun!"

Her Father said rather anxiously, "But won't your Stepmother expect—? And your Stepsisters—?"

"Oh, they're not up yet," Ella reassured him. "Come along, Father, sit down—do! It's so nice to have you a bit to myself."

"Is it, child?" He was only too glad to be persuaded, and sat down at the table while she darted about, snatching up tablecloth, cup-and-saucer, knife-and-spoon, bread-and-butter, teapot-and-milk-jug, running from the table to the dresser, the dresser to the larder, and the larder to the table again, which she laid with all the things that go to make breakfast.

"And how have things been, eh, while I've been away?" asked the Father, easing his stiff legs. "Not too bad?"

"Not too bad, Father."

"Well, that's a good thing, eh?"

"Yes, Father. I'm so glad you're back. I have missed you."

"Have you, child?"

"The house isn't the same thing without you."

"Isn't it, child?"

"There!" laughed Ella, putting the last touch to the table. "Here's your coffee, your honey, your butter, your rolls; in fact, Father, here's your breakfast!"

"And where's yours, Ella?"

"Mine?" Ella hesitated for half a fraction of a split second, so perhaps he didn't notice. "I'll have mine all in good time," she said, and went on quickly. "Tell me all your adventures. Is the city you went to very fine and grand? Did you meet any ogres and dragons?"

"Not so much as a goblin," said the Father, buttering a roll.

"What a pity!" cried Ella.

"There's a nice thing for a daughter to say!" chuckled the Father. "So you want your old dad to be gobbled up by an ogre, do you?"

"No, no, Father!"

"Or changed into a frog, do you?"

"No, no, no!"

"Ogres and dragons indeed!" He saw her bubble with laughter. Things couldn't be so bad, then, after all. He dropped another lump of sugar into his coffee. Outside in the snow the horse let out a whinny.

"Oh, poor Dobbin!" exclaimed Ella. "He wants *his* breakfast. I'll just go and give him his oats."

She jumped up, and the Father rose from the table. "I'll come too. I forgot to unload the saddlebags." But Ella pushed him back into his seat.

"*I'll* unload them. Your coffee will get cold."

"Then my coffee can be heated up again." (He wasn't going to have any of *that*.) "Those packs are much too heavy for a girl like you."

"Nonsense, I'm as strong as Hercules!" boasted Ella. (*She* wasn't going to have any of that, either.)

"You should just see me heaving sacks of coal and buckets of water." She doubled her fists to her shoulders to show how strong she was.

The Father looked at her. All the breakfast fun went out of him; he wilted like a pricked balloon. "Sacks and buckets, do you—eh?" he murmured.

But she pretended not to hear, and drew him outside, chattering. "It will be fun undoing the saddlebags. I wonder what's in them. Did you bring back some presents for my Stepsisters?"

(It simply won't do for *all* the balloons to be pricked.)

CHAPTER III

Presents for Crosspatches

FOR A LITTLE WHILE the Clock ticked and the Tap dripped on in the empty kitchen. A mouse ventured out of its hole in search of crumbs. A rat began gnawing a pumpkin lying in a corner. Then somebody came sneaking down the stairs so stealthily that two lizards who had come out for air didn't notice until a shadow fell across them and sent them scuttling into their crevices in the wall. The mouse darted back into its hole, and the rat took cover behind the pumpkin.

The stealthy somebody was Ella's Stepmother; she enjoyed getting up early to take people by surprise when they thought she was asleep in her bed. Araminta and Arethusa were still snoring in theirs; they could be as unpleasant as a dose of medicine when they chose to, but they never chose to get up early to be it: and the Stepmother, who doted on and spoiled them, let them lie abed as long as they liked. But she wasn't going to pamper Cinderella— for Cinderella was what she called her husband's daughter, with a sneer on her lips. Sometimes she shortened it to Cinders, but never to the child's real name of Ella. She had sneaked down on purpose to pounce, only stopping to put on her dressing gown and bedroom slippers, and her second-best wig. She never let anybody see her without it, because under it her head was as bald as a billiard ball. The tall wig bobbled and nodded as she snooped and slithered down the stairs, intent on spying out some fault she could punish Cinders for. First she tried the bed. No doubt the idle chit was still enjoying her sleep and neglecting her duties.

"Up with you, lazybones!" The Stepmother twitched off the blanket. But she was disappointed; nothing was there except a little picture in an oval frame. The snarl on her face changed to a nasty smile as she put it in her pocket.

Next she tried the sink, and out of the pile of washing-up she snatched a saucer so sharply that it

got chipped on the tap. "Cracked! One of my beautiful saucers cracked!" She could haul Cinders over
the coals for *that*, at all events.

Next she slithered over to the fire and glared
at the cheerful glow upon the hearth. "Blazing like
blazes! At this hour!" She grudged the comforting
warmth which Cinders had already enjoyed, and
shoveled off half the lumps of coal before crossing
to find fault with the breakfast table. And there she
found as many as her heart desired. "Coffee! Butter!
White bread! *Honey!*" This was the last straw.
"HONEY!"

"Who's there?" asked Cinderella at the door.
The glare from the snow outside dazzled her eyes,
and she stood blinking over the top of a huge parcel
in her arms.

"Who's there, who's there?" mocked the Stepmother. "Well may you ask who's there, you care-
less, greedy, idle, extravagant—"

"Stepmother," pleaded Ella.

"Don't call me Stepmother, call me madam,
slut."

"Yes, madam," faltered Ella.

"Who said you could eat honey?" The virago
advanced on Ella in her bobbing wig.

Ella backed away, murmuring, "Stepmother—madam—"

"Who said you could drink coffee?"

"Madam—" whispered Ella.

"Or eat white bread instead of black, you glutton? Or help yourself to butter, you thief, you sloven?"

"Madam, madam!" Ella dropped the parcel and took flight round the table, the Stepmother after her. At that moment the Father came in, lugging Dobbin's saddlebags. He let them fall on the floor at the Stepmother's feet, obliging her to stop. Ella took the chance to slip into the chimney corner. The Stepmother stared icily at the Father.

"So you've come home, have you?"

"Yes," said the Father with a timid little laugh. "Yes, wife, I've come home."

"Home to the kitchen," sneered the Stepmother. "Hardly the place for gentry, I should have thought."

"Really, my dear, here's a welcome!"

"Hoity-toity! What sort of a welcome have you given me? I should have thought it was customary for a husband to salute his wife when he comes home from a journey."

"I've hardly had time, my dear."

"And how much time does a kiss take, pray?" The Father kissed her cheek meekly. "*That* didn't take much time."

For want of something better to do, he lifted the heavy parcel onto the table. "And what is *that*?" demanded the Stepmother.

"Just a few knickknacks I picked up in the city."

"For me?" cried the Stepmother.

"For you and the girls."

"Presents!" The Stepmother's face turned red with excitement; her greedy eyes glittered. "Presents for me and the girls? I dote on presents!" She shouted up the basement stairs, "Araminta, come down! Come down, Arethusa! Presents!"

From the bedroom above two grumbling voices answered, "Oh, Ma! You've woke us up!"

One of the voices drawled, "You've spoiled my beauty sleep." (That was Arethusa.)

The other voice whined, "You've ruined my dream." (Araminta.)

The two voices drawled and whined together, "It isn't ten o'clock yet."

"Come down at once!" shouted the Stepmother. She turned on Ella, who had taken scissors to the parcel. "Never cut string, wasteful!" Then she slapped her. Then she tried to untie the string and broke her fingernail. Then she glared at her husband as much as to say it was *his* fault; and then she snatched up the bread knife and cut the knots herself. She was tearing off the paper avidly just as her two daughters flopped and slopped down the stairs in their sloppy, floppy wrappers. They yawned and rubbed their eyes as they came, to show how ill-treated they were.

Arethusa was stupid and greedy and fat and flouncy. She had her hair in curlpapers; her pink wrapper had a lot of cheap lace about it, badly torn and very dirty; most of the buttons had come off, and the hem was undone in two places; she had used a whole packet of safety pins to pin the hem up and pull the front together, and the torn lace was held in place by eleven brooches out of Christmas crackers.

Araminta was peevish and sly and thin and scratchy. Her hair was in six plaits no thicker than rat tails; her mustard-yellow wrapper was stained with bacon fat and egg yolk, and her bony elbows were so sharp that they poked through holes they had made in the sleeves.

In spite of all this Arethusa considered herself a dream of beauty, and Araminta thought herself the tip-top of fascination. They were spiteful to Ella, scornful of their Stepfather, and ill-humored with their Mother. Nothing contented them, and one was just as silly as the other.

"Oh, Ma, what *is* all the fuss about?" grumbled Arethusa.

"You might let a person have her sleep out," sniffed Araminta. "You might have more thoughtfulness for a person's nerves."

"You know how it upsets me to be waked so sudden," said Arethusa, shuffling to the breakfast table and dipping her thumb in the honey pot. "I'm as sensitive as a plant, that I am." She sucked her thumb and wiped it down her dressing gown.

"Thusy darling, Minty sweet, my precious pair!" cooed their Mother. "Your Stepfather's come home."

"What if he has?" said Arethusa. "You know I'm no good without my twelve hours."

"You're not much good *with* it," said Araminta.

Arethusa pinched Araminta.

"Don't you pinch me, you nasty fat lump!"

"You shut up, you horrid old splinter!"

"*I'll* give you splinters!" Araminta crooked her nails. Arethusa doubled her fists.

"My pets, my pets!" cried their Mother. "I didn't wake you for nothing. Your pa has not come back empty-handed." She displayed the parcel, with its contents bursting through the torn wrappings.

The Sisters pounced upon it, screaming, "Presents!"

"Pa, Pa!" cried Thusa. "Did you bring the silks and satins I said about?"

"And my sapphires and rubies?" cried Minta.

"And my sugarplums?"

"And my ostrich feathers?"

"Everything," the Father assured them. "I remembered everything. So that's all right, eh?" He smiled anxiously at Ella, who had slipped back into her corner, and hoped she was smiling at him from the shadows.

The Sisters were crumpling and rumpling the contents of the parcel on the table. Arethusa dragged out two gleaming dress lengths crossly. "*Blue* satin! *Pink* silk! I distinctly said for blue silk and pink satin. It *is* disappointing."

Araminta was examining some glittering jewelry spitefully. "A *ruby* necklace and a *sapphire* tiara! Didn't I tell you sapphire necklace and ruby tiara? I *do* call it a shame."

The crosspatches made faces at the Father and threw the presents on the floor.

"I'm very sorry," he said. "I tried all over the place, really I did—but it's better than nothing, eh?"

"I think nothing is better than a disappointment," sulked Arethusa.

"You mean you think nothing is *worse* than a disappointment," snapped Araminta.

"No I don't, do I, Ma?"

"Yes she does, Ma, doesn't she?"

The Stepmother tried to soothe them. "Never mind, pets, look at these scarves—and these laces, and these fans!"

Araminta made a sudden grab. "There's my ostrich feathers!" She stuck them round her head.

"There's my sugarplums!" Arethusa snatched a bagful out of the muddle and crammed her mouth with sweets.

"Give everybody one, dear," said the Stepmother.

"What for?" asked Arethusa.

"It shows a nice nature."

"Oh, all right," said Arethusa glumly. "There's one for you"—she popped a sugarplum into the Stepmother's mouth—"and one for you"—she did the same to the Father—"and one for you"—she put her tongue out at Araminta as she pushed the sweetmeat in, and went to Ella, standing on the hearth—"and one for—the fire!" She threw Ella's sugarplum into the flames, saying, "Yah!"

"What a sense of humor!" said the Stepmother fondly. "You want your breakfast, you poor neglected pets. Don't stand there idling," she said to

Cinderella. "Get their breakfast at once."

The Father ventured mildly, "Ella hasn't had hers yet."

"She can finish the milk in the jug." The Stepmother looked into the jug of yesterday's milk. "Why, she *has* finished it, the greedy-guts!"

"I gave it to Tabitha," said Ella.

"If you gave it to Tabitha that's *your* lookout. Lay the trays for my daughters, and see they have plenty of coffee, and butter, and white bread—"

"And cream and brown sugar—" said Thusa.

"And scrambled eggs on toast—" said Minta.

"And HONEY!" said the Stepmother, shepherding her daughters toward the stairs. "Come along, pets."

At that moment a tremendous fanfare of trumpets broke the silence of the snow outside the window.

CHAPTER IV

Invitations to the Ball

"WHAT'S THAT?" demanded the Stepmother.

Araminta and Arethusa had already flown to the window and were making white blobs of their noses against the panes.

"Look, look!" squeaked Araminta. "It's a man!"

"It's a man!" squealed Arethusa. "Don't push me."

"I'm not pushing. It's a grand man!"

"A *very* grand man!" gasped Arethusa. "You *are* pushing."

"I'm not! You're shoving *me*."

"That's right, dig your skinny elbows into my

poor ribs. I'll be as blue as blackberries tomorrow."

"Go on, shove your great shoulders into my backbone, do! I'll be as black as blueberries to-night."

Another fanfare trumpeted from the road. The girls' eyes gobbled up the red-and-gold figure outside the window. "Ma, Ma! It's the grandest man you ever saw. You never did see such grandness!"

The Father looked over their shoulders and said, "It's the King's Herald."

"Never!" cried the Stepmother, running to the window and pushing all three out of place.

"And the King's Trumpeter in front," said the Father, "and the King's Footman behind with a sackful of letters."

"Ma, Ma!" squealed Arethusa. "Do you think he's got a letter for us?"

"Ma, Ma!" squealed Araminta. "He's giving us the go-by!" She made a dash for the door, calling, "Hi, hi! Here we are!"

"Here we are! Hi, hi!" echoed Arethusa.

The Stepmother dragged them back. "What are you thinking of? We can't receive the King's Herald in the kitchen."

But the mischief was done. The King's Herald, who had been looking about for the front door, supposed this was it. He made a sign with his haughty forefinger to the Trumpeter. The Trumpeter kicked the door open and marched in, blowing a still louder fanfare as he came. The Herald followed him—a grand man indeed! So elegant in his deportment that a swan would have looked clumsy beside him, so richly beribboned and gold-laced that a peacock would have shut its dingy tail for shame. The Footman was hardly noticeable as he entered last, in spite of his satin sackful of letters.

"Ladies!" The Herald removed his feathered hat and made three bows, completed by three flourishes; each bow was deeper than the one before, and each flourish swung the hat higher to the ceiling.

The ladies curtsied as elegantly as they could in their floppy dressing gowns.

"Sir!" said the Stepmother.

"Sir!" simpered Araminta.

"Sir!" gulped Arethusa, catching her bedroom slipper in her untidy hem and grabbing a chair back so as not to topple over.

The Herald's manners were as superior as his appearance. He seemed to notice nothing, and gave Arethusa full time to recover her balance before he pronounced, "I come on the King's business."

The King's! The Stepmother pulled herself together and, waving a regal hand to the basement stairs, said in her company voice, "Shall we proceed to the parlor?" She could not bear so genteel a gentleman to suppose that she and her daughters frequented the kitchen.

The Herald was, however, so self-sufficient that he had no need to suppose anything whatever. "The kitchen suffices," he assured her. "Time presses."

The Stepmother supposed, nevertheless, that he was supposing all manner of things. "You catch us, as it were," she explained, "at an unlikely hour."

"Apologies on apologies for the inconvenience." The Herald's flourish swept the ceiling.

"Sir!" The ladies' curtsies swept the floor, but this time Arethusa held on to the chair before she went down.

The Herald came to the point. "I have, you understand, three thousand invitations to deliver before midday."

"Invitations?" said the Stepmother, pricking up her ears.

"To us?" asked the Sisters, clasping their hands.

"To every eligible female in the land," replied the Herald. The Trumpeter blew a fanfare that made the crockery rattle in the sink.

The Stepmother grabbed each girl by the wrist and presented them as if they had been at Court.

"My daughters, sir! Arethusa." Arethusa bobbed. "Araminta." Araminta ducked. Their wrappers flew open, revealing their nightdresses. The Stepmother observed, "They are not, so to speak, up yet."

"The fault," said the Herald politely, "is mine." He addressed the Sisters. "You are not married?"

"Oh no," giggled Arethusa, "not in the least."

Araminta sniggered. "Do we look it?"

"True, ladies," agreed the Herald. "I might have guessed." He signaled the Footman; the Footman advanced and opened the mouth of the sack. The Herald dipped in a finger and thumb and produced a large ivory card, printed in gold. "Allow me." He presented the card to Arethusa, dipped again, and presented a second card to Araminta. "Permit me."

Bursting with excitement, the Sisters read in turn.

"The King commands—"

"Your presence at a ball—"

"At the Royal Palace tonight—"

"At ten o'clock."

"Fail not at your peril!" they read together.

"Incomparable phraseology!" breathed the Stepmother. The King! A ball! At the Palace! What could this sumptuous invitation portend?

The Herald had not yet finished with the sack.

He brought forth a third card, which he presented to the Stepmother. "Parents are requested to attend."

His gesture included the Father, who ventured to ask, "And what, sir, is the purpose of this function?"

"The King seeks a bride for his son. At the ball she will be selected."

The Herald signed to the Footman to close the sack; and having performed his duties, relaxed sufficiently to glance about him. His eyes fell on a little figure in the shadows. "Who is that by the chimney?" he inquired.

The three ladies stopped gloating over their cards, and their gleeful faces became grumpy ones.

"That?" Arethusa tossed her head. "She don't count."

"She's nobody," sneered Araminta.

"Everybody, in the King's eyes, is somebody," said the Herald. "Who is she?"

The Father said timidly, "She's Ella, sir, my—"

But the Stepmother squashed him. She wasn't going to have this superior personage connect her with the kitchen slut. "She's just the Stepsister, sir. She cleans the steps, you know."

The Herald addressed himself to the little figure. "Your name is Ella?"

"Yes, sir," she answered shyly.

"You are unmarried?"

"Yes, sir."

"*She* can't come to the ball!" spat Araminta; and Arethusa fumed, "It'd spoil everything!"

The Herald dipped into the sack again and extended a gilt-edged card to the little figure. "Your invitation, Miss Ella." The ladies dared not protest. "I have my duties. I perform them. All cards to be presented at the gates. No admittance without one. Ladies!" He bowed so low that his topknot brushed his shoe buckle. "Your servant!"

The Trumpeter blew a fanfare. The Footman opened the door. The Herald passed outside into the snow. His attendants followed him. The door closed.

Dazed with happiness, Ella stood looking at her gold-edged invitation. Her eyes were so blurred with tears of joy that she could not read the golden words on the ivory. But she knew what they were. "The King commands your presence at a ball. . . . At the Royal Palace tonight. . . . At ten o'clock."

Nothing so wonderful had happened to her since her Mother died. It was too wonderful to be true!

CHAPTER V

The Miniature

OH YES! It was too wonderful to be true—and it wasn't *going* to be true, if Minta and Thusa knew it! They pranced toward Ella, one on each side, mincing and bowing and mimicking the Herald. "Your invitation, Miss Ella!—Miss Ella, your invitation!"

Minta twitched the precious card out of Ella's hand and dashed across the room. But this was more than Ella could put up with. She chased Minta fiercely, crying, "Give it to me! Give it to me!" and snatched the invitation back.

Minta sneered, "There's manners!" and Thusa

said, "*I'll* give her manners!" and they prepared to set about their little Stepsister, who hugged the ivory card against her breast and trembled half with terror, half with anger.

"Thusa! Minta! Shame on you!" protested the Father.

The Sisters turned for support to their mother, who never failed them; but to their surprise she pointed to the door. "Go upstairs and get dressed, pets," she said smoothly.

"But Ma—"

"Go—up—*stairs!*" commanded the Stepmother.

When she used that tone of voice she had to be obeyed. They shuffled upstairs, sniffling and sniveling.

"And you too," said the Stepmother, turning to the Father.

"Me, my dear?"

"You need a wash."

The Father glanced from his wife to his little daughter. "Don't you think, my dear, we might first settle—"

"You—need—a—*wash!*"

The Father too knew better than to disobey. Murmuring, "Well, perhaps I do, after my journey, eh?" he ambled out. But as he passed Ella he thrust a roll furtively into her apron pocket, whispering, "For breakfast." He disappeared up the back stairs to the upper floor, leaving Ella to the Stepmother's tender mercies.

"Now!" said the Stepmother.

Ella put her hands behind her back.

"Don't try to hide that card."

"I won't give it you," said Ella, edging away. "I won't!"

"*Madam,*" said the Stepmother.

"I won't give it you, madam," repeated Ella, in a low voice.

"I am not asking you to give it to me," said the Stepmother in her sweetest tones, which were twice as nasty as her sharp ones. "But you know you can't go to the ball, don't you?"

"Why not?"

"I should have thought *that* was clear enough," cooed the Stepmother. "You don't think they really *want* a little slut like you, do you?"

"Why not?"

"And you think you *could* go?"

"Why not?"

"Because you've got nothing to go in. Have you?" Ella did not answer. "Do you want to stand among the silks and satins with people laughing at you? *Do you?*" The Stepmother paused for the answer that did not come. "Tear up that card!" she commanded.

"I won't," said Ella.

"You'll be sorry."

"I won't."

"We'll see about that," said the Stepmother. "What do you think this is?" She held up her hand with something in it.

"My mother!" cried Ella. "My miniature! Where did you get it? Give it back!"

"And what do you think *this* is?" The Stepmother picked up the rolling pin.

Ella went on crying wildly, "Give it back to me, give it back! You took it from under my pillow."

"You will tear up that card," said the Stepmother, flourishing the rolling pin, "or there will be a little smash. Do you want to see your mother's picture smashed?"

"It's the only one—" whispered Ella.

"What a pity," said the Stepmother. "Tear up that card before I've counted three. One! Two!—"

Ella tore the ivory card in half.

"Little pieces," said the Stepmother. "Half isn't enough. Little pieces."

Ella tore the card across and across; she went on tearing till it was a mere handful of white-and-gold confetti. On one of them she could just make out "a ball." She tore the ball up too.

"That's a good sensible little girl," cooed the Stepmother. "Now put the little pieces in the fire. They'll warm you up nicely. *Go on.*"

Ella put the Royal Invitation into the fire. There was a little gleam, a few gold sparks, and the King's ball went up the chimney in a puff of smoke. The Stepmother flung down the rolling pin. "You see how I keep my promise. There you are." She handed back the miniature to Ella, who clasped it to her heart; she had feared that even now the Stepmother might smash it. But the Stepmother was cunning; the miniature put Ella in her power. She would be able to find it again when she wanted to, and now she could make the child obey her forever.

From an upper room the Sisters were wailing, "Ma! Ma! Ma!"

"What is it?" shouted the Stepmother.

"Cinderella hasn't lit the fire!"

The Stepmother turned on Ella with the smile that was worse than a scowl. "There, child, you hear? You haven't lit the fire. And of course there's no wood in the box. You used it all on your own fire, didn't you? Minty and Thusy can freeze, but Cinderella must keep warm, mustn't she? Well, you can keep warm in the snow." All the false sweetness dropped off her as she took Ella roughly by the shoulders. "Out you go! Don't stand there blinking at me like an owl. Go out this minute and get sticks to warm my poor dear shivering daughters. And be quick about it, or—" She kicked the rolling pin with a little laugh. "Or it won't be pleasant, you know."

She thrust Ella toward the door and slopped upstairs in her flapping bedroom slippers.

Ella stood still where she had been pushed, her thoughts spinning. *I wish I could be like the others. . . . I wish nobody ever scolded anybody. . . . I wish I wasn't frightened of stepmothers. . . . I wish I didn't feel cold. . . .*

She pulled herself together and gave herself a talking-to.

"This won't do, Ella. It won't—just because you can't go to the ball. Put on your shawl, silly, and be sensible. Lots of people all over the world can't go to balls. If you've got to get sticks, you've got to get sticks." She went to the door through which the King's Herald had appeared like a glorious dream and then faded forever. Beyond the frozen coach road the white trees, with their trunks of ivory and their branches of lace, stretched away in alabaster silence. *The woods look lovely in the snow,* thought Ella. *I wish . . .* she thought. *And the snow looks lovely in the woods. I wish . . . How lovely it would be if everything was lovely*, thought Ella.

She went out into the snow, thinking, *I wish . . . I wish . . .*

CHAPTER VI

Brushwood and Sticks

THE SNOW looked lovely in the woods, and the woods looked lovely in the snow, but oh! it was bitter cold. Robin Redbreast and Jenny Wren shrank in their feathers and huddled together on an icy branch, so cold and so hungry that it was a question whether they would starve or freeze to death first. They had flown round in circles trying to find one withered berry left among the snowdrifts, and now they had abandoned hope.

On the path below their bough an old crone was shuffling her way, bent double beneath a faggot of brushwood that her numb red fingers had been gathering together for the past hour. It was almost more than her aged back could bear, but if she had no fire to warm her bones, how could she live? She seemed as feeble as the birds in the tree, and the fringe of the thin brown shawl that covered her head looked much like Jenny Wren's bedraggled feathers, and sheltered her as little from the cold.

"Brushwood and sticks!" muttered the Crone, shambling her weary way. "Brushwood and sticks! The faggot is heavy, my backbone cricks. Crick, crick, crickety-crick, will nobody help me to carry my stick? Alas and alack! The pack on my back! My ribs they creak and my joints they crack! Crack, crack, crackety-crack, will nobody help me to carry my pack?" muttered the Crone. But nobody heard her, so nobody answered. She gave a heave of her poor thin shoulders, and the faggot slipped to the ground.

"Down, faggot, down," she groaned. "I can no furder go. Welladay, I shall just sit here and watch the birds, who be no better off than old me. Hop away, Robin! Pick and pry, little Jenny! Tweet and twitter, tiny tit! *Tweet-tweet!*" The Crone crouched on a fallen log and rubbed her bony red fingers. Now and then she said *"Tweet-tweet!"* to the birds, for fellowship, for that was all they had to share between them.

"*Tweet-tweet!*" said the Crone. "*Tweet-tweet!*"

"*Tweet-tweet, tweet-tweet!*" answered a voice among the trees. "Pretty bird, pretty dick! *Tweet-tweet!*"

Through the white woods came Ella, seeking brushwood for the fire. Not so much as one fallen bough could she spy, not a twig or a handful of fir cones. It was as though an army of wood gatherers had been before her and carried it all away; yet she dared not go home empty-handed.

"Perhaps if I weren't so hungry, I would search better," she said to herself. "That's it, of course! I haven't had any breakfast. No wonder my eyes aren't just the thing. There's a tree stump I can sit on for a dining chair. It's covered with the most beautiful snow-white satin, and its legs are of twisted ivory—no queen could sit at breakfast on a more splendid throne!" Ella brushed off just a little of the cold white satin, however, before she sat down on her throne; and then she pulled out of her pocket the roll of bread her father had given her on the sly.

"Dear Father!" She smiled. "A horseshoe—that's for luck. I'm going to be lucky today." She broke the roll into two pieces and considered them gravely. "Now, let me see. This half is a slice of game pie. That half is three peaches. No, it isn't, it's *four* peaches. I *am* being lucky. It might have been only three." Ella looked from one half to the other and decided, "I'll begin with the pie." She nibbled a crumb. "How delicious! What thick pastry! What rich jelly!"

"*Tweet-tweet!*"

"Oh, Robin, what a feeble twitter!" cried Ella, looking to see the poor little bird that had roused her pity. "Pretty Robin! Pretty Jenny! Can't you spy any titbits for *your* breakfast? I know breakfast isn't easy when it's as freezy as this."

"*Tweet-tweet!*" The twitter was fainter than ever.

Ella stopped nibbling her slice of jellied game pie. "All right, if you're as hungry as all that. Good-by, my pastry-pie!" She crumbled the half of her roll between her fingers, and scattered the crumbs like a shower of snowflakes under the tree. Down flew Robin, down flew Jenny, and picked them up rapidly, twittering for joy. Ella watched her breakfast disappear between their beaks, and then crumbled the second half of her horseshoe. "Good-by, my four peaches! Aren't you lucky dickies! It might have been three."

A little cackle of laughter greeted this remark. Ella looked round, surprised. It couldn't have been the birds.

"Did anyone speak?" she called.

"I'm cold," came a whisper behind her, "and I'm old."

"Someone *did* speak!" said Ella, jumping off her stump.

The whisper came again, scarcely stirring the air. "It's bleak, and I'm weak."

Ella looked behind her, her heart beating a little faster; then her fear vanished in a sigh of relief. "It's only a funny old Crone."

The Crone's gray head was shaking as if she had an ague. "It's chill, chill, and I'm ill, ill. Up, faggot, up!" she moaned. "For furder I must go. Fuel and fire! Fuel and fire! Heat is my comfort and my desire." She staggered to her feet and stooped for her faggot again, croaking, "The burden is bitter, the load is cruel, will nobody help me to carry my fuel?"

Alas! Before she could hoist the faggot onto her shoulders, it slipped out of her hands; the withes that bound it came undone, and the sticks scattered in all directions. The disaster was too much for the old woman, who could only stand wringing her hands and wailing, "Oh deary me! Oh deary deary me!"

"Don't cry, Granny!" Ella came running to her, eager to help. "I'll pick up your sticks for you."

The Crone peered out from under her tattered

shawl. "And who may you be when you're at home?"

"I'm nobody when I'm at home," laughed Ella, "but when I'm out I'm whoever I like. A countess, a duchess, a princess!"

"Are you indeed?" said the Crone. "And what may you be now?"

"Now I'm a Good Fairy—see, here is my wand!" Ella picked up a long, slim branch and waved it over the scattered sticks. "Hey presto, sticks! Be a faggot again!" As she spoke, and before she could stoop to sweep the sticks into a bundle, they flew together of their own accord and became a faggot bound fast with the withes as before.

"Oh—Granny!" said Ella faintly. "Did you see that?"

"Did I see that?" said the Crone. "Of course I seed that. I got eyes in me head, an't I? Well, 'tis a lucky day when one meets a Good Fairy on the way, hey, hey? Jest hoist the faggot on my back agen, do 'ee?"

"I'll carry it for you, Granny," said Ella. "My back's younger than yours. Where are you going?"

"Home," said the Crone.

"And who are *you* when you're at home?" asked Ella gaily.

"Ah," said the Crone, wagging her head, "I'm

somebody when I'm at home. But when I'm out I'm anything I like. A wren, a robin, a tit."

"And what may you be now?"

"Only a funny old Crone."

Ella turned very red and looked abashed. "Oh, Granny, please forgive me—please do."

"What for, child?" asked the Crone in the sweetest voice in Fairyland. And when Ella, startled, looked up, she wasn't there.

"Oh! Oh—where are you?" she cried.

Out of the air the answer came: *"Tweet-tweet!"*

"Granny! Was it you tweet-tweeting all the time? Oh Granny, come back! You've forgotten your faggot."

"Tweetit! Tweetit! Keep it and eat it!" came the answer out of the air.

"Keep it?" cried Ella joyfully. "Oh, thank you, thank you! Now I shall have plenty of wood to take home. But—*eat* it!" She laughed. "How can I?" She stooped to lift the faggot, and never had faggot of that size weighed so heavy. *How funny,* she thought. *It doesn't feel like only sticks. There's something inside it.*

Kneeling down in the snow, she pulled the faggot open and peeped into it. The sticks parted so that she could slip her hand right down into a little hollow in the middle. There *was* something inside it! She brought out, one by one, four beautiful peaches! But that wasn't all; in went her hand again, and out came a game pie, covered with thick pastry and oozing with jelly. Ella rubbed her eyes, unable to believe them. But the peaches and the pie were still there. "Granny!" she called faintly. "You've forgotten your breakfast."

Out of the air the same sweet voice replied, "Keep it and eat it! Keep it and eat it! Tweetit, tweetit! Keep it and eat it!"

"Thank you, thank you, thank you!" cried Ella joyfully.

She sat down again on her white satin throne, her pie on her knees, her peaches in her hands, with now a bite of pastry, and now a mouthful of sweet, dripping fruit. The robins, the wrens, and the tits flew down in dozens, picking at the crumbs scattered around her, and the woods looked really lovely in the snow.

CHAPTER VII

The Prince and the Zany

THE PRINCE sat in his dressing room, gazing into a picture frame. The Zany sat at his feet, gazing at the Prince.

The picture frame was shaped like a heart and was made of pure gold. On top, in the dip of the heart, perched a golden cupid, and the point of the heart was planted in a golden rose; the cupid had diamond-tipped wings, and in the heart of the rose was a pearl of great price. But the Prince was gazing into nothing, for the beautiful frame was empty.

"Zany!" sighed the Prince.

The Zany, as pleased as a dog to be spoken to by his master, stood on his head and gazed at the Prince upside down.

"Dear Zany, in another hour the ladies are coming."

The Zany turned head over heels and gazed at the Prince right end up.

"She—*she* is coming!" said the Prince.

The Zany pressed his hand upon his heart.

"But who *is* she? Oh, Zany, who is *she*?"

The Zany ruffled his hair and gazed mournfully into the air.

"Well," said the Prince, "my heart will know her when my eyes behold her. Oh, Zany, how my heart is beating!"

The Zany laid his head on the Prince's heart and listened—then clapped his hands over his ears as if deafened, and rocked to and fro.

"Doesn't it throb?" asked the Prince.

The Zany rocked harder.

"Doesn't it gallop?"

The Zany rocked so hard that he toppled over.

"Doesn't it burn?"

The Zany sat up, blew on his burned fingers, and shook them in agony.

The Prince said impatiently, "Stop talking, do! I never heard such a chatterbox."

He gazed into the empty picture frame, and the Zany gazed at the Prince.

CHAPTER VIII

Dip! Dip! Dip!

"ATTEND, GIRLS!" said the Stepmother.

She was seated between Arethusa and Araminta in their boudoir, where they were preparing to prepare for the ball. Each sister had a dressing table to herself, littered with combs and brushes and hand mirrors and trinket stands and pincushions, besides all sorts of rubbish such as bits of ribbon they would never wear, and bits of artificial flowers they wouldn't throw away, and broken strings of beads they wouldn't mend, and wrappings from the sweets they were always sucking, and lots of spilled powder of every shade from pearl pink to peony red, and a muddle of tinsel, lace edging, frayed feathers, soiled garters, and scent bottles without any stoppers and stoppers without any scent bottles. Two gaudy new ball dresses were hanging over a screen, and the Sisters, in calico wrappers, were waiting for their baths, which they were not at all fond of; but the Stepmother had insisted that for once her darling pets should go fresh and clean to the Palace.

They were looking rather sulky, therefore, as she read aloud to them from a book of Court manners which she had got out of the library, for none of them had been to Court before or had the least idea what was expected of them.

"This is important, girls," said the Stepmother. " 'Directions for Behavior in the Presence of Kings, Queens, and Peers of the Realm.' "

"You've read us so many directions already, Ma," grumbled Arethusa, "that my poor head's all of a fluster."

"Do you wish to be a success at Court, or do you not?" demanded the Stepmother. Arethusa pouted. "Very well then! We now come to 'RULES ABOUT COUGHING: To cough at a party is to indicate that either you are ill, and should not have come, or bored, and had better go home. It is better to choke than to cough.' "

"What for?" asked Arethusa, starting to cough.

"She's coughing on purpose, Ma," said Araminta.

"Choke it down," commanded the Stepmother.

Arethusa did so, going purple in the face; on which Araminta sniggered, "*I* think it's better to cough than look like a boiled beetroot."

"Who's a boiled beetroot?"

"You're a boiled beetroot!"

"Ma, Ma! Minta's calling me a boiled beetroot!"

"I daresay the Prince is very partial to boiled beetroot," said the Stepmother, and returned to her book. "Next comes 'RULES ABOUT SNEEZING: Sneezing, even more than coughing, should be suppressed in the Presence of Royalty. If you feel one coming—' "

"Oh, Ma! I feel one coming!" gasped Araminta.

" 'Hold your breath—' " read the Stepmother.

Minta held her breath.

" 'Grit your teeth—' "

Minta gritted her teeth.

" 'Clench your fists—and subdue it at all costs. It is better to break a blood vessel than to sneeze.' "

Minta stopped gritting and clenching and

sneezed violently. "*I'm* not going to break no blood vessel," she declared.

"I hope the Prince is partial to water-spouting whales," remarked Arethusa.

"Who's a water-spouting whale?"

"You're a water-spouting whale."

"Ma, Ma! Thusa's calling me a water-spouting whale."

"Shall I *ever* teach you manners?" snapped the Stepmother. She rustled through the book again. " 'STARING: Never Stare. . . . CONTRADICTING: Don't Contradict. . . . YAWNING: Stifle it. . . . SCRATCHING: Grapple with it. . . . SECOND HELPINGS—' "

"Second helpings of what?" asked Thusa hopefully.

" 'Second Helpings of Anything must be refused,' " read the Stepmother. "Ah! This is what I was looking for—'CURTSYING: Curtsying should be swanlike. Everything depends on the Dip.' Let me see you dip, girls."

The girls got up from their chairs and flopped down on the floor, like buckets bumping down a well.

"More swanlike," said the Stepmother. "One, two, three, dip! One, two, three, dip! You *must* think of swans."

"I *was* thinking of them," said Arethusa.

"So was I," said Araminta.

"And I was thinking of geese," said the Step-mother. Really, her precious pets were being extra trying today. "Do you want to be wallflowers?"

"What's a wallflower?" asked Arethusa.

"A wallflower is a young lady who sits all night with her back to the wall because nobody will ask her to dance. Dip, girls, dip! One, two, three, *swans*, not wallflowers."

"*I'm* not going to be a wallflower." The Sisters pranced about, practicing curtsies. "Nobody's not going to ask *me* not to dance, so there!"

"Nobody's going to neglect *me*," said Arethusa.

"Nobody's going to reject *me*," said Araminta. "I'm going to be the most beautiful bloom in the whole of the room, so there!"

"Excepting for me! People will pass the remark, 'She's just like a hothouse rose'—so there!"

Minta tossed her head. "If I don't get lots of introductions, look out for ructions!"

"If I don't get first prize for airs and graces," said Thusa, "I'll smack their great big ugly faces. *I'm* not going to be a wallflower!"

"No more am I not going to be a wallflower!"

"So *there*!" The Sisters flopped on the floor in a heap, with not a curtsy left between them.

Ella came timidly to the door. "The bath is ready, madam."

"Dip, dip, dip!" said the Stepmother.

The Sisters gathered themselves up, piled Ella's arms with towels and soap and sponges and perfume and rubber ducks, and pushed past her to the bathroom, where she had to scrub their backs for them. They were much too lazy to do it for themselves.

CHAPTER IX

Tch! Tch! Tch!

THE FATHER peeped into the boudoir and said, "My dear!"

The Stepmother was studying the book of manners, where she had got as far as "Etiquette for the Elderly." She was not sure what an etiquette was, but she thought it was some sort of underskirt, and was wondering whether her new ball dress had got one.

"My dear!" said the Father again.

The Stepmother looked up, and frowned when she saw that he was carrying his coat in his hand.

"What sort of behavior is this? Coming into a lady's boudoir in your shirt-sleeves?"

"I'm sorry, my dear, but my coat needs a stitch."

"What if it does? Do you expect a lady on the verge of presentation to demean her fingers with a needle?"

"But my dear! You wouldn't like me to go to Court with a split seam?"

"Who said I would?" snapped the Stepmother. "Ask the servant to mend it."

"The servant?" repeated the Father.

"You know. Thingummy. Cinderella."

"Ella is my daughter," said the Father quietly.

"A dutiful daughter should be only too delighted to put a stitch in her father's coat." She raised her voice to screech, "Thingummy! Thingummy! (*Just like the screech of a parrot,* thought the Father.) But the screech was drowned by the splashing from the bathroom, so she changed her note, and bawled, "CINDERELLA!" (Just like the bellow of a bull.)

Ella came to the bathroom door. "Yes, madam?"

"Have you done my precious pets' backs and shoulders?"

"Yes, madam."

"What are they doing now?"

"Playing with their rubber ducks, madam."

"Then heat the curling tongs, fill the warming pans, brush up the hearth, sweep the snow from the front steps, and come and mend your Father's coat before you start dressing my precious pets for the ball. Do you hear?"

"Yes, madam."

The Stepmother turned and glared at the Father. "You might have spared me the trouble of raising my voice. If I'm hoarse as a crow when the Prince says 'How-de-doo?' it will be *your* fault." She tucked the book of manners under her arm, and said loftily, "I shall go to my lubrications."

Left alone in the boudoir, while his little daughter was no doubt fulfilling orders as to curling tongs and warming pans and all the rest of it, the Father wandered here and there, muttering to himself, "Tch! Tch! Tch! 'Yes, madam, yes, madam.' . . . 'Thing-ummy.' . . . 'Yes, madam.' Tch! Tch! Tch! One of these days I shall lose my temper." He hung his head as he said it, for he was ashamed of himself for not having lost his temper long ago. Just an old coward, that was what he was. He paused before a charming mirror hanging on the wall. "Think of it, only think of it! I brought that mirror from Italy for her Mother when Ella was a baby. I remember . . ." He looked into the glass, remembering the beautiful face that had been mirrored there. He wandered across the room to the silken couch, sat down on it, and gently stroked its curved head. "And this—I brought it from France when Ella's Mother was ill. Her hair lay just here, as she rested with Ella in her arms. . . . 'Thingummy! Yes, madam!' Tch! Tch! Tch!"

"Give me your coat, Father."

Ella sat down beside him and took his coat, as if she hadn't noticed his head bowed on the place where her mother's head had rested. Perhaps she hadn't—eh? She was stitching away cheerfully at the torn seam, saying, "It's just a little rip. A few stitches will soon put this right."

He nodded and passed his hand across his forehead.

"Have you got a headache, Father?"

"No, no, Ella. Just thinking."

"Now don't go thinking too much," said Ella lightly. "It doesn't always do."

"Doesn't it, Ella?"

"No, Father—it does *not*," said Ella between the stitches.

He did not answer, but watched her nimble fingers.

She chattered on without looking at him. "Mind you notice everything at the ball tonight, Father, won't you? *Everything*. Every speck. The dresses, the dancing, the lights, the music, the feast, the Prince. And tomorrow morning—*early*—will you creep downstairs and tell me all about it? Will you, Father?" She bit off her thread. "Do you mind?"

The Father said eagerly, "You'd enjoy that, would you—eh?"

"We'd enjoy it together," said Ella gaily. "Come along! Stand up."

He stood up, and she helped him on with his coat, pulling and patting it deftly into shape. It was an old coat (the ladies' new dresses had cost a mint of money), but Ella's fingers seemed to flatter it into being as fine as a new one; and she teased the old shirt ruffle, which she had washed and goffered that morning, into a handsome frill all down the front. Then she stood back a little, head on one side, and said, "There!"

They smiled at each other, and the Father bent his head.

"Cinderella!" screamed Arethusa from the bathroom.

"Cinderella!" shrieked Araminta.

"CINDERELLA!" bellowed the Stepmother.

"Yes, madam, yes, madam, I'm coming,

madam!" Ella ran off to the bathroom as fast as she could.

" 'Yes, madam!' " whispered the Father. "Tch! Tch! Tch!"

His head was drooping again as he stole away.

CHAPTER X

They Are Dressed for the Ball

ARETHUSA sneaked into the boudoir from the bathroom. She hadn't stopped to dry herself properly and dripped as she came; she wanted a chance to pry into Araminta's beauty secrets, and shuffling over to her sister's dressing table, she began to sample the contents of all the bottles and boxes. One little pot that took her fancy she concealed in her fat hand. The next moment her hand was slapped so smartly that she yelled.

"Fingers, fingers!" Araminta hadn't stopped to dry *her*self either, and she dripped all over Arethusa as she spoke. "That's *my* dressing table, thank you. Leave my pots and pomatums alone."

Arethusa blustered, "I was only—"

" 'I was only, I was only—' " mimicked Araminta. "You was only, was you, was you only, you was?" She grabbed the pot out of Arethusa's hand.

"Don't snatch!" said Arethusa.

"Don't snitch!" retorted Araminta. "You can go to prison for snitching."

"If it comes to snitching, who snutch my Circassian Cream?"

"Who snutch my Essence of Ispahan?"

"Who snutch my Milk of Morocco?"

"Who's got a face like a turnip?"

"That's not an argument," said Arethusa.

"What's not an argument?"

"That isn't."

"Well, what *is* an argument?"

"What do you mean, what *is* an argument?"

"What do you mean, what do you mean?"

"Oh, shut up!" shouted both girls together.

The Stepmother bawled from the bathroom, "Birds in their little nests agree."

The little birds flounced back to their own dressing tables and began to examine themselves in the mirrors, as Ella came back loaded with the soaps and scents and powders they had been using in the bath.

"Come on, Cinders, hurry up," said Thusa.

"Look sharp, can't you?" said Minta.

"I'm looking as sharp as I can," said Ella.

"Then look sharper," said Arethusa. "Do come and dress me, for goodness' sake."

"Me first, me first," said Araminta.

"I'm oldest," said Arethusa.

"I'm first alphabetically," said Araminta.

"Don't get so flustered," said Ella. "You're spoiling all your fun. *Enjoy* getting dressed for the ball."

The Sisters repeated in tones of astonishment, "Enjoy it!"—and Araminta remarked, "You can't go through life enjoying things."

"I could," said Ella.

"Then why don't you?"

Ella didn't answer. It was such an easy answer; but if she had told Araminta the truth she would have had her head bitten off. If only—if *only* the Sisters would sometimes allow her to enjoy herself! If only, if *only* she could dress herself for the ball, as well as dressing them. But what was the use? She held her tongue, and began to brush and curl Araminta's stringy hair.

Arethusa, meanwhile, had forgotten about being the oldest and was gazing fondly at her own reflection in the looking glass. "There's no doubt about it," she cooed. "I really *am* going to be rather a dazzle tonight. What a boon is beauty! Don't you rather dote on droopy eyes?" she asked of nobody in particular. "The dear Prince will never be able to resist them. I'm afraid, Minty, *your* eyes aren't a bit droopy."

"Nor my mouth, darling," sneered Araminta.

Arethusa pretended not to hear, but called, "Cinders!" so sharply that Ella flew to her side and began powdering her back. Araminta didn't seem to notice, for now *she* was staring lovingly at herself in her own looking glass.

"No," she decided, in satisfied tones, "not droopy. Mine is what I should call a mysterious allure. What is it, what *is* it about me? That's the question the dear Prince will keep asking himself. There certainly is a hidden something."

"Completely hidden," agreed Arethusa.

"How do you do, dear Prince?" murmured Araminta languishingly.

"Dear Prince," gushed Arethusa, "how do you *do*?"

"How do you do, ladies?" said Ella gaily, making a deep bow to each of them.

"Oh, but how sweet of you!" simpered Arethusa, accepting an imaginary bouquet. "Roses! I dote on roses."

"So much prettier than wallflowers," observed Araminta.

"Who's a wallflower?" demanded Arethusa.

"Look in the looking glass," said Araminta. She turned her back, and continued her own conversation with the Prince. "Music? Yes indeed! I dote on music. I know it backward."

"Backward?" scoffed Arethusa.

"Backward," repeated Araminta firmly.

"Ho!" said Arethusa. She waved away the refreshment the Prince was offering her. "Ices? No, thanks," she cooed. "What are ices when I can feed on your face?"

"Feed on his face?" tittered Araminta.

"Feed on his face," repeated Arethusa coldly. Then she forgot the Prince and rumpled her messy dressing table, asking, "Where's my pink ribbon?"

"Where's my beauty spot?" asked Araminta.

"Where's my yellow feather?"

"Where's my fan?"

The Stepmother sailed in, fully dressed for the ball. She threw up her hands to see her daughters still in their petticoat bodices, pushing their tawdry litter of finery this way and that. "Girls, girls, don't dawdle. The Prince is all impatience for you. Do you want him to ask somebody else for the first dance?"

"Cinderella's such a slowcoach, Ma," complained Arethusa. "Look at my feather, it's gone all crooked."

"My beauty spot's on the wrong side, I knew it was," grumbled Araminta.

"Straighten that feather! Change that patch!" scolded the Stepmother. "Be quicker, can't you? Clumsy!"

"Clumsy, clumsy," echoed the two Sisters, while Ella, flying from one to the other, did her best to see to them both at once.

The Father came to the door to say, "The carriage is ready. Wrap up well. It's freezing."

"Whose fault is that?" snapped the Stepmother. "No more dilly-dally, girls. Off we go."

"But Ma! We're not finished yet."

"Then you must finish in the carriage."

"That's easy, isn't it?" said Minta. "Jog, jog, jog! That carriage wants new springs."

"Only he's too mean to buy 'em," said Thusa, making a face at the Father. "Jolt, jolt, jolt!"

The Sisters bounced and jigged up and down on their dressing stools. "Jog, jog, jog! Jolt, jolt, jolt!"

The Stepmother tied a scarf over her tall wig, saying, "Oh very well, if you *want* to be late."

"Oh, very well," mimicked Araminta, "if you *want* us to catch our deaths! Where's my cloak?"

"Me first, me first!" cried Arethusa.

"Cinders, where's our cloaks?" they screamed together.

Ella came running with them, and they snatched them out of her hands; but in their hurry Araminta snatched Arethusa's, and they bickered until they got the right ones, and then they dragged them on back to front and bickered some more, and then they flung them on upside down and bickered worse than ever.

"The horses hate standing," murmured the Father.

"Come this instant!" insisted the Stepmother. "Come as you are."

"Without our bouquets? Where's our bouquets?" The Sisters flew about with their cloaks dragging after them half on, half off.

Ella crept up to the Stepmother, who stood tapping her foot in a frenzy of impatience. "Madam?" she whispered.

"What is it?"

"Couldn't I—" faltered Ella. It wasn't a good moment to ask, she knew, but when was it ever a good moment? And it was now or not at all. She plucked up her courage, and said again, "Couldn't I come just as far as the Palace gates?"

The Stepmother stared at her as a parrot might stare at a black beetle. "With *us*?"

"Just to watch the people going in?" pleaded Ella.

"Watch the people going in?" repeated the Stepmother, as if her ears had deceived her. "Certainly not. Girls, girls, what *are* you looking for *now*?"

They were chasing each other and everything else round the room, pulling off covers, slamming drawers, shuffling the things on the dressing tables, the chairs, and the mantelpiece.

"My Essence of Pearls!" gasped Arethusa.

"My Extract of Lilies!" gasped Araminta.

"My Magnolia Water!"

"My Oleander Balm!"

"My lollipops!"

"What d'you want lollipops for?" asked Araminta.

"Suck on the way," said Arethusa.

"You exasperating couple!" cried the Stepmother. She drove the girls before her; there was a scuffle; and the litter on the dressing tables was swept to the floor, combs and brushes, powder and paste, beads, ribbons, pomatums, and all the rest of it. All three turned as one on Ella, saying furiously, "CLUMSY!"

Ella dropped down on her knees to pick up the mess. She saw them disappearing through the door, on their way to the ball. "Have a good time!" she called in a trembling voice. They didn't seem to hear. She scrambled to her feet and ran to the top of the stairs. Their trains were swishing into the passage below, the trains that would soon be swishing up the Palace steps. "Good-by!" she called down the staircase well. "Have a good time."

The front door banged.

CHAPTER XI

Bells Over the Snow

SHE STOOD and listened to the horses' bridle bells ringing over the snow.

For the past hour she had been listening to the jingle of thousands of horse bells, as coaches and carriages, sleighs and sledges, berlines and barouches rolled silently along the coaching road in the snow that muffled the trot of the horses' hoofs and the grind of the wheels. The ground was soundless under its thick white blanket, but in the crystal air the bridle bells tinkled like icicles, and the coachmen's whips cracked sharp as ice splitting on a frozen pond. The bells she had heard were ringing

hundreds of girls to the ball. Inside their convey-
ances they sat in all their beauty, dressed in silk and
gauze and satin and brocade, adorned with pearls
and moonstones and diamonds, shod in gold and
silver, wrapped in velvet and furs. Pretty as pictures, they sat up stiff and still, that their glossy
curls, befeathered and beflowered, might not be
disarranged. In her mind's eye she had seen them
every one, all so lovely that how could the Prince
choose among them? The bells were like a tinkling
chain linking her with the Royal Palace, her only
link with the ball where she would have been the
happiest of them all, if she might only crouch behind a pillar in the corner and look on.

Then for a little while the bells stopped ringing,
for the ladies had started in good time and were out
of hearing. Now they must nearly all be riding up
the sweeping carriage drive, alighting at the marble
steps to the Palace doors, mounting them daintily
in their gilded slippers, brushing the snow crystals
a little with the edges of their ermine mantles, en-
tering the glittering hall on purple carpets. Now
they were hearing their names called at the entrance
to the ballroom, beyond which stood the Prince,
bathed in light, waiting for them all, yet waiting
for only one. She had never seen the Palace or the

staircase or the lights, she had never seen a ball of any sort, but she could imagine every detail as she listened to the bells over the snow. The one thing she could not imagine was the Prince.

When the ringing ceased, when the last vehicle from far away had passed far away again, she was too busy attending to the Sisters to imagine anything: so late they were, such a to-do there was! But even helping them with their heavy gowns of maroon and mustard yellow, powdering them, dressing their hair, finding things for them—even that was still a little part of the ball she wasn't allowed to go to. She could hardly bear it as the departure grew nearer, and so she had dared to plead that she might just see the people going in. She could have crouched outside in the dark and listened to the music and the laughing—and that would still have been a part of the ball. When she was refused, she clung to the last few minutes of the spilled finery, the hasty scramble out of the house, the little squeaks and shrieks on the slippery path: *"It's freezing! It's freezing! Go carefully! Hang on to me! Stop gripping me! You're tripping me! Oops! Ma was nearly down that time! I'm petrified! I'm paralyzed! Stop dragging me! Stop nagging me! I'm dithery! It's slithery! OOPS! Ma was really down that time! We'll be late,*

*we'll be late! Look alive, look alive! The horses are
waiting at the end of the drive.* . . . " It was still a
part, a little part, of the ball. . . .

No more slipping and slithering, no more
squeaks and shrieks . . . The carriage door banged,
the coachman cracked his whip, the bells began
again, jingling fainter, fainter, fainter over the snow.

She pressed her ear to the cold windowpane.
She could still hear them . . . still hear them . . . hear
them . . . now they were gone, the last bells ringing ladies to the ball.

CHAPTER XII

Ella All Alone

IT IS DIFFICULT, sitting alone in a dark vaulted kitchen, with all the rooms of an empty house overhead, and all the silence of the night outside—it is very difficult to pretend that you are not alone. It seemed to Ella, with her head on her arms on the table, that she had never been quite so alone in all her life. *Nobody upstairs,* ran her thoughts, *nobody downstairs, nobody inside, nobody outside, nobody anywhere at all but me.*

The truth was that even Ella wasn't there; her tired little body was, but her heart had flown away through the night to try to peep in at the golden windows of the Palace. No wonder the little body felt alone, without even its own heart to keep it company.

The tiniest scratching sound under the wainscot fell on her ear, just by the corner where the mousehole was.

"Mousey, mousey!" Very softly Ella got down on her knees on the floor. "Would you come on my hand?" She crept toward the hole, as secretly as the mouse itself, holding her hand out. Would it come? "Would you, mousey?"

But the mouse, who had ventured forth as Ella approached, disappeared like a shadow into the other shadows in the room. Ella dropped her hand and tried not to feel disappointed. "I expect she's run away to a grand Mouse Ball. Yes, of course. There will be a King Mouse, and a Queen Mouse, and a Prince Mouse and all, and a Lady Mouse, and a Slavey Mouse, dancing at the ball."

The unexpected rhyme at the end cheered her up a little and set her thoughts dancing. "They *must* have some mouse music," she decided. She knew just the thing, too. Among the broken ornaments on the high mantelpiece was a toy musical box that long ago had tinkled pretty tunes. It still had a tinkle or two left in it, if you turned the handle carefully, and although they stuck a trifle here and there, the

tunes were pretty still. Quite gay now, Ella carried
the musical box to the table, and as she turned the
handle, she imagined the scrubbed tabletop was a
shining dancing floor in a grand mouse palace. She
began to describe it to herself, speaking aloud to
the jerky, tinkly tune.

> "First comes the King Mousey,
> With a gold crown on his head. . . .
> Next comes the Queen Mousey,
> Looking very sleek and well fed. . . .
> Then comes the Prince Mousey
> In a wee pink satin coat,
> And a wee rose in his paw,
> And a wee squeak in his throat. . . .
> All round the kitchen ballroom
>   the mousey ladies twitter,
> And scatter and scutter and skitter.
> 'Will the Prince ask me, ask me, ask me,
> Will the Prince ask me to dance?'
> But the Prince doesn't give one of them,
> Not one of them,
> Even a glance.
> 'Please, please, Miss Mouse,
> Miss Slavey Mouse,
> Will you have a spin?'
> 'Yes, yes, Prince Mouse, yes, yes,

Do let's begin!'
Round and round and round and round and round!
The Lady Mousies squeak, 'Oh dear! Well I never!
    What a pity!'
But the King Mousey and the Queen Mousey squeak,
    'Isn't she pretty!
Isn't she pretty! Isn't she pretty! Isn't she . . . ' "

Something stuck in the musical box, and something stuck in Ella's throat, and neither of them could go on. Ella stifled the choke in her throat and buried her face in her hands, where the choke turned into a sob or two. "I want to be upstairs like I used to be," sobbed Ella.

A voice behind her said, "I used to be upstairs too."

She didn't have to look round to know who *that* was. "Did you, Grandpa?"

"You wouldn't remember," said the Clock. "You couldn't so much as walk when your father brought back that gilt clock from Paris. So downstairs I came. I think I've had a sort of pain in my pendulum ever since."

Now Ella did look round, saying sympathetically, "Oh dear!"

"And it *was* oh-dear, I can tell you," said the Clock.

"The maids used to treat me without any respect. Yes, yes, it *was* oh-dear till you came downstairs too."

"Me, Grandpa?"

"It's horrid for you in the kitchen, *we* know. But if it isn't nice for you, it is for us."

"Nice for you?" said Ella wonderingly.

"Much nicer than what we might have. Much nicer than what we have had. Your hands are so kind when you polish me. What do you say, Chair?"

"Your body is so light when you sit on me," said the Rocking Chair. "What do you say, Fire?"

"Your eyes are so bright when you look in me," said the Fire. "I like seeing my little flames in your eyes."

All round the room the voices of the Things were saying, "We like having you about, we like having you about."

"You're kind to Things," said the Clock.

"We like you, we like you, we like you," said the Things.

Ella looked round at the Cups and the Plates and the Taps and the Fire Irons and the Brooms, and said, "I like you—all of you."

"And we're sorry you're not going to the ball," said the Clock.

The voices chimed in, "Very sorry, very sorry, we're very, very, very sorry."

"Don't remind me!" Ella implored them. "Don't remind me! I did want to go to the ball! Why can't I? I want to go to the ball like my sisters. Oh, Grandpa, ten o'clock!" she cried, turning her face toward his. "Just on ten o'clock! It's beginning, and I'm not there."

"Steady," said the Clock. "I'm just going to strike."

"Don't strike, Grandpa, don't!" begged Ella.

"My dear, I can't help it."

"Can't you? Please! Couldn't you hold in?"

"It would hurt."

"Badly?"

"Very badly. And then—I shouldn't even be in the kitchen."

"Go on—" Ella gulped down her tears. "Strike!"

The Grandfather Clock began striking ten. At the fourth stroke, something happened.

CHAPTER XIII

She Is Dressed for the Ball

"TWEET-TWEET! Tweet-tweet!"

Ella rubbed her ears, and then she rubbed her eyes. The glass in the clock case had lit up like a lamp, and crouched in the light was the funny old Crone Ella had met that morning in the woods.

"Why, Grandpa—Granny," she whispered.

"Tweet-tweet!" twittered the Crone, and then the light went out as suddenly as it had appeared.

"I'm dreaming." Ella pinched herself; she *must* be dreaming. "Did you say anything, Grandpa?" she asked timidly.

But he only went on striking the hour, and at

the last stroke of ten the clock case lit up again—
and this time, instead of the Crone, an enchanting
Fairy hovered in the light, with butterfly wings and
a star-pointed wand.

"I *am* dreaming," whispered Ella.

The Fairy stepped out of the clock. "Why
dreaming?" she asked.

"It's so wonderful," said Ella. "Waking things
are sad."

"Waking things can be wonderful too," said
the Fairy.

Ella gazed at her in bewilderment. "You mean
you're *true*?"

"As true," said the Fairy, "as that you are going
to the ball."

"I—? Going to the—? Like my sisters?"

"Not at all like your sisters," said the Fairy
rather tartly. "As if I couldn't do better than that!"

"But my dress," stammered Ella. "Look at me!
My hands—look at them! My hair—look at it! Don't
you see—"

"Of course I see," chuckled the old Crone's
voice. "I got eyes in me head, an't I?"

"Granny?" gasped Ella. The voice had undoubtedly come out of the Fairy's pretty throat.
"Granny, Granny! Oh," she said, abashed, "I beg
your pardon, madam."

"If you call me madam I'll slap you," said the Fairy.

Unable to contain herself for joy, Ella danced about the room, laughing, "Slap me, slap me, do what you like to me, I love you, Granny, *tweet-tweet!*"

"That's better," said the Fairy.

"But—" Ella shook her puzzled head. "You look so young for a granny."

"I'm as old as the hills," said the Fairy. "I was old when *your* granny was a baby."

"Did you know her?" asked Ella, wondering.

"Yes."

"And my Mother?"

"Yes."

"You knew my Mother!"

"She left you in my care," said the Fairy.

"She—! Me—! You—!"

"And so," said the Fairy, "you are going to the ball."

Ella clasped her hands, saying sorrowfully, "I haven't got an invitation card."

"Really?" said the Fairy. "What's that you are clasping so tightly in your hands?"

Ella undid her fingers, and there, between them, was an ivory card printed in gold letters. " 'The King commands your presence—' " she read in a daze. "I'm going to the ball! How wonderful!" Laughter rippled through her lips again. "I'm going to the ball!" Waving her precious invitation card, she danced round the kitchen, curtsying to the Rocking Chair, to the Fire Irons, to the Brooms, to all the Things in turn. "I'm going to the ball!"

"Now listen to me," said the Fairy.

"How wonderful, how wonderful!" said Ella, curtsying to the Clock.

"Child! Are you listening?"

"I don't know—I think I am—I don't know," said Ella.

"If you don't listen, you'll be sorry," the Fairy warned her.

"I'll never be sorry again. How wonderful!"

The Fairy held up her hand. "The wonder will last till exactly twelve o'clock. No less and no longer. Isn't that so, Grandpa?"

"That—is—so. That—is—so," ticked the Clock.

"When you get to the ball—" the Fairy went on.

"Oh!" cried Ella. "But when I get there my stepmother and my stepsisters—"

"Won't know you," said the Fairy. "No one will know you. No one will guess that the Princess from Nowhere is the slavey from the kitchen. Isn't that so, Grandpa?"

"That—is—so," ticked the Clock. "That—is—so."

"The Princess from Nowhere? Me? But Granny—" Suddenly Ella remembered the cruel mockery the Stepmother had poured upon her, and she hung her head. "Look at me! I don't want to stand among the silks and satins with all the people laughing at me. I don't want to be called a little slut before them all. I don't want—"

"You don't want this, and you don't want that! What *do* you want? Make up your mind."

"I *do* want to go to the ball."

"Then suppose you leave it to me," said the Fairy.

She lifted her wand and began to speak in a voice like music, that was not the voice of either the old Crone or the fairy voice in which she had been speaking till this moment. It was a magic voice, like one heard perhaps in a lovely dream, forgotten as soon as one wakes. While she spoke, music streamed out of the air and the fire on the hearth, and down from the ceiling and up from the stone flags on the floor; and the star on the wand, moving up and down and in and out, glowed now green, now blue, now silver, now gold, and what a moment before had been a cold dark vault became veined like a rainbow as the Fairy summoned her spirits.

> "Earth, air, water, fire,
> This child attire.
> Gold fire, silver water,
> Dress your daughter.
> Green earth, blue air,
> Make her fair.
> Water give grace, fire give light
> To her tonight.
> Air give her joy, earth give her flowers,
> She is ours.
> Earth, air, water, fire,
> Our child attire."

Down from the vaulted ceiling, up from the flagged floor, out of the taps over the sink, and the flames on the hearth, floated the spirits, blue and green and silver and gold, enveloping Ella in light. She did not know what was happening, only, as in the lovely dream, she felt her rags fall away, and saw her hands and arms and feet become as white as snow, and her hair as smooth as sunlight on a rippling sea; and while the charm went on around her, the spirit voices sang in her ears such music as she had never even imagined.

"Gold fire, silver water,
Dress our daughter.
Green earth, blue air,
Make her fair.

Jeweled fire, silken water,
Dress our daughter.
Flowered earth, feathered air,
Make her fair.

Glittering fire, shimmering water,
Dress our daughter.
Flowering earth, fluttering air,
Make her fair."

Marvelous things were happening to Ella. Garments of materials so exquisite and so fine, jewels so pure and so sparkling, such as were to be found nowhere in the world, arrayed and adorned the little Princess from Nowhere. And Ella, standing as still as a snow statue, let it happen, only sighing, "Oh, oh, oh! I'm losing my senses."

Through the rainbow cloud came the Fairy's warning voice. "Keep your senses, Ella. You will need them."

And somewhere beyond the cloud she heard Grandpa booming, "Twelve o'clock! Remember twelve o'clock!"

Then the voices that had been singing so radiantly turned sad and pale.

> "Cold fire, frozen water,
>   Poor daughter!
>   Withering earth, shivering air,
>   Where? . . . Where? . . . "

Ella felt a shiver pass through her body from head to foot. "What is it, Granny? Oh, Grandpa, what is it?"

"Nothing to fear," came the Fairy's voice through the cloud that was thinning away like mist. "You will dance and be happy, you will sing and be gay—"

"Yes, yes," cried Ella, "I will be happy and gay!"

"But always remember that just before midnight you must take your leave."

"Oh, Granny, not so soon," pleaded Ella. "Let me stay a little later. *Please.*"

"Stay if you like. But at midnight the wonder will vanish. Your shining dress will fade like leaves in autumn, your glowing jewels will crumble into ashes, and the Princess from Nowhere will be the slavey from the kitchen again. Isn't that so, Grandpa, isn't that so?"

"That—is—so," ticked the Clock.

Around her the spirits were dissolving, for their task was done. But their voices as they went were radiant again.

> "Gold fire, silver water,
>   Behold our daughter!
>   Green earth, blue air,
>   See! How fair!"

Oh, indeed how fair was the little figure standing in the middle of the dark kitchen, clothed in a dress that seemed to be spun of light, that flowed like air and water as she moved, into which were woven the most delicate flowers of spring. It seemed impossible that those immortal flowers should fade like autumn leaves.

The hands of the Clock were pointing to eleven; but before the hour struck he boomed once more the warning: "Remember twelve o'clock!"

"It doesn't matter, it doesn't matter!" cried Ella. "I shall have a whole hour at the ball. A whole hour. Sixty minutes, thousands of seconds. Look at me, Kitchen! Look at me, Chair! Look at me, Brushes and Brooms! Is my dress pretty?"

"Pretty! Pretty! Pretty!" cried the Things.

She ran to the Clock, crying, "Grandpa, Grandpa, look at me! Can you see me?"

"I see you, little barefoot," said the Clock.

Ella stared down at her tiny bare feet in dismay. The spirits who dressed her had forgotten the shoes. "Oh dear!" she sighed.

"Suppose you look at *me*," suggested the Clock.

"At you, Grandpa?"

"Inside me. Look inside me."

"What for?"

"A present."

She opened the clock case eagerly. Under the pendulum stood the two tiniest slippers in the world. Wonder of wonders! They were made of glass. Ella was awestruck. Glass slippers!

"Put them on," said the Fairy.

"Granny! *Glass slippers!*"

"Do they fit?"

"Yes!" breathed Ella, before she had even tried. They fitted exactly, from her rosy heels to her toes. She skipped with glee. "I'm going to dance—for a thousand seconds—in glass slippers!" She flew to the door.

The Fairy asked, "Where are you off to?"

"The ball, the ball!"

"Run through the snow in glass slippers?"

Oh dear! Oh no! But how?

"In your coach, of course," said the Fairy, reading her thoughts.

"I haven't got a coach."

"Haven't you?" The Fairy pointed her wand at the pumpkin in the corner. In the twink of an eye it became a crystal coach, lined with white satin.

"Oh, Granny! But I haven't any horses."

"No?" The Fairy pointed her wand at the mousehole in the wainscot. Out of the hole trotted eight mice, who as they appeared changed into milk-white horses with silver manes and tails.

"A coachman?" stammered Ella, unable to believe her eyes.

Out of his own hole pattered the big rat; in another second he became a burly coachman in a three-cornered hat and a cape braided with gold. A last wave of the wand, and down from the damp wall dropped the two lizards, who as soon as they touched the floor turned into two elegant footmen, bowing and scraping.

"Way for the coach of the Princess of Nowhere!" called the Fairy.

The whole of the kitchen wall seemed to dissolve; the crystal coach stood on the snowy road, the gold-trimmed coachman and footmen leaped to their places, the horses shook their milk-white heads, and the bells began to jingle on their bridles.

"Way for the coach of the Princess of Nowhere!" cried the Things in the kitchen.

"Oh," whispered Ella, "listen! The bells are ringing."

The Fairy opened the crystal door of the coach, and Ella sprang into the ivory satin seat. The footmen folded their arms across their chests. The coachman cracked his whip. The horses pranced.

"Have a good time!" cried the Things. "Have a good time!"

"Twelve o'clock!" boomed Grandpa. "Twelve o'clock!"

But Ella did not hear his warning boom; she only heard her own bridle bells, ringing her to the Palace over the snow.

CHAPTER XIV

"Way for the Ladies!"

THE HANDS of the Royal Clock above the Palace doors were pointing to ten. On each side of the splendid entrance hall tall windows threw long stripes of light across the terrace on which the Palace stood. The ornamental staircase which curved upward to the terrace from the gardens was thronged with arriving guests. Behind the rows of windows lay, on one side, the anterooms to the throne room and, on the other, the Royal Orangery, where the orange trees bloomed, even in winter, some in white flower and some in golden fruit.

This was the Prince's favorite spot when he

wanted to be alone. He strolled there dreaming of the loveliest lady on earth, who would one day be his bride and walk beside him to the altar with folded hands and downcast eyes, crowned with blossoms from one of these very trees. Which one? That evening the Prince, on his way to the throne room, paused by each tree in turn, sniffing it delicately. Behind him came the Zany, snuffing vigorously. The Prince twined some of the flowers into a wreath and threw it away because there was no bride to wear it. The Zany put it on his head and walked beside the Prince with his hands folded and his eyes cast down. Presently the Prince took notice of him, and the Zany grinned hopefully; but the Prince said crossly, "Do stop being such a silly Zany. She won't look a bit like you." The Zany's grin faded; he took the wreath off his head and tried to stick the blossoms back on the orange trees. When the petals dropped to the ground he hid his face in his hands and hoped he was crying, but it was no use; he could not cry real tears or laugh real laughter; he could only reflect whatever the Prince was feeling, like a mirror in which the tears are not wet and the laughter has no sound.

The Prince walked on to the throne room to meet his guests. The Zany trotted after him like a dog.

Pretty girls in their hundreds and thousands had been gathering there for the past hour. Only the six prettiest were still to come. They were ladies of high birth, and knew better than to arrive early and be lost in the crowd; though of course they would not be later than ten o'clock, because to be unpunctual is bad manners.

As the Prince made his way to the dais on which the throne stood, he could hear the Herald marshaling the arrivals in the hall.

"Way for the ladies! Way for the ladies! All admission cards ready! Fair ladies to the right, dark ladies to the left. Move along, please, move along! Way for the ladies!"

The Herald's voice sounded both important and disdainful. He came of very good family and had been rather spoiled at home. When he was offered the post of the Prince's Herald he flattered himself that he could make an art of it by performing his duties with elegance and eloquence; nevertheless, all he did and said was tinged with haughtiness, because he considered those duties a trifle beneath him.

"Fair ladies to the right! Dark ladies to the left!"

But as he waved the ladies left and right, he contrived to make the fair ones wish they were dark, and the dark ones wish they were fair. He even looked with faint displeasure on the last six beautiful aristocrats who appeared on the final stroke of ten, and kept them waiting in the hall while he presented himself to the Prince.

"Your Royal Highness, the ladies have been sorted."

"Sorted?" said the Prince.

"Sorted, sifted, separated, collected, and classified."

"With what object?" asked the Prince.

"A special selection will sup at Your Royal Highness's own table: the elite, the nonpareil, the crème de la crème, the unparalleled and not to be excelled, the most superior—in short, the least inferior."

"How many?" asked the Prince.

"Six," said the Herald.

"Present them," said the Prince.

He spoke calmly, but his heart was beating wildly as the six aristocrats were waved in his direction. One of these, surely, must be the lady for his heart-shaped picture frame.

The Herald announced, "Her Magnificence the Marquise of Cinnamon!"

The Marquise of Cinnamon, exquisitely gowned, sank down in a deep curtsy, and the Prince's heart sank with her. It was not She. His eager speech died upon his lips, and he said politely, "I am delighted to meet you."

"Her Supremacy the Countess of Caraway!" announced the Herald.

Down went the Countess, and down went the Prince's heart.

"I am overjoyed to receive you," he said.

"Her Transcendency the Baroness of Allspice!"

"How charming of you to come," said the Prince.

"Her Pomposity the Archduchess of Cochineal!"

"The pleasure is mine," said the Prince.

"Her Arrogance the Viscountess of Cloves!"

"I hear it is positively freezing," said the Prince.

"Her Exuberance the Margravine of Mace!" announced the Herald.

"I trust it will eventually thaw."

The six aristocrats, having made their six curtsies and received their six flat greetings, retired a little till they should attend the Prince at table. The Herald, having announced the ladies, prepared to announce the supper.

But what was all this bustle at the entrance? A last party of guests had arrived, unpardonably late; and, still more unpardonably, they were hustling and bustling into the throne room, in a scurry and a flurry and a huddle and a muddle highly unsuitable to the occasion. They had not even the common courtesy to wait for the Herald at the door—and what a party! The three ladies were of unexampled ugliness, their dresses in outstandingly vulgar taste; and as for the elderly gentleman who followed them meekly, his identity, thought the Herald, was pure nonentity. He dimly recalled having seen these persons somewhere that morning, and having forgotten them as quickly as he could.

With an air of authority the Herald barred their progress to the throne and extended finger and thumb for their invitation cards, while they gabbled their names in his averted ear.

"Miss Arethusa!" he announced. "Miss Araminta! And their Mother! And Father—"

"No, no, no, you got it wrong!" burst out Arethusa.

"Our Father? Him?" snickered Araminta. "He's only our Stepfather."

"And *Step*father!" announced the Herald, deeply affronted.

Arethusa pushed past him, bounced up to the Zany, and gurgled, "How do you do, Prince?"

"Dear Prince," simpered Araminta, shoving Arethusa aside, "how well you're looking!"

The Zany made a face at them, and the Sisters were charmed with the familiarity; but the Stepmother felt that something was amiss and, curtsying to the Zany, said, "Excuse the error."

The girls were pointing their fingers here and there. "Ma, Ma, look at the lights! Look at the shiny floor! Look at that fat man with a gold hammer— Ma, Ma, what's he got a hammer for?"

But the Stepmother had spotted the Prince at last, and all she muttered was, "Dip, dip, dip!" Thusa and Minta achieved their clumsy curtsies, and by clutching each other managed not to fall flat on their faces. The Prince waited politely till they had got on their feet again, and then said coldly, "Let the supper be served."

"Let the supper be served! Let the supper be served! Let the supper be served!" proclaimed the Herald.

The fat man knocked his gold hammer three times on a little knocking block, which he had invented for the purpose, and always carried in a handy pocket; the rich curtains at the end of the room swept apart, and the sumptuous supper table stood revealed.

CHAPTER XV

"Here's a Health!"

THE FAT MAN with the gold hammer was the Toastmaster. He was as short and round as the Herald was long and slim, and his heart was as soft as the Herald's was stiff. But then he had not come of a Good Family, like the Herald. He had got his post at Court on the strength of his voice, which besides being strong was as rich as cow's cream. He had rolling eyes, which at the sight of a lady, of *any* lady, melted like butter; even Arethusa and Araminta made them melt like margarine. He thought ladies were made to be loved, and he loved them all. This meant that he loved each of them only a little bit, but by being careful he made his love go around. He had never yet loved any lady with his whole heart.

He found it difficult not to do so, however, when he took his stand behind the special table where the Prince sat among the six aristocrats. They were the most beautiful ladies by far who had ever come to Court, and the Toastmaster could not decide whether he loved the Marquise of Cinnamon's curls more than the eyebrows of the Countess of Caraway—or the white hands of the Baroness of Allspice more than the rosy lips of the Archduchess of Cochineal—or the sparkling eyes of the Viscountess of Cloves more than the shell-like ears of the Margravine of Mace. How could one be fondest of any of these beauties? One could only be fondest of them all.

But look! The Boar's Head was being brought in on a silver salver. No more sentiment! The Toastmaster's duties must begin. He rapped his hammer three times, cleared his throat, and sang the toast to the Boar.

"Here's a health to the Boar,
The bristle-backed Boar,
The bristle-backed Boar who's given his head
To honor our spread,

Our prodigal spread,
His buffeting head, to honor our spread.
Last week in the forest he roamed like a lord,
And now the wild Boar is lord of our board.
The Boar,
The Boar,
The lumbersome, blundersome Boar
Who rules the roast
Shall be our toast
From floor to roof and roof to floor."

"The Boar!" said the Prince, lifting his glass.

"The Boar!" shouted the guests, tossing off theirs. Then they fell to, some with a greedy clatter of knife and fork, some picking daintily. Arethusa and Araminta had three helpings each, and sucked their greasy fingers so as not to miss one speck of the succulent gravy. The Prince ate nothing, but dropped morsels of meat from his plate to the floor, where the Zany sat out of sight under the tablecloth. He ate the scraps eagerly, and kissed the Prince's shoe buckle.

And now, on an ivory platter, the roast Peacock appeared, with his broad fan of green and gold and blue feathers spread behind him. The Toastmaster trolled his toast as lovingly as if the bird were a Court beauty.

"Here's a health to the Peacock,
  Imperious Peacock,
    Imperious Peacock appearing
full sail
  With eyes in his tail,
  Astonishing tail,
Full fluttering sail, with eyes in his tail.
He strutted about like a king on the sward,
And now the proud Peacock is king of our
    board.
        The Peacock,
        The Peacock,
  Unparagoned, arrogant Cock,
    This bird of boast
    Shall be our toast,
  With *hic* and *haec* and *haec* and *hoc*."

"*Hic, haec, hoc!*" echoed the Prince, glass in air.

"*Hic! Haec! Hoc!*" clamored the guests, draining theirs; and the clatter of knife and fork began all over again. Arethusa and Araminta picked their wing bones in their fingers. The Prince let a gleaming tail feather flutter under the tablecloth, and the Zany stroked it and stuck it behind his ear. Then he cocked the ear to hear what came next.

The Toastmaster's hammer was rapping in the Trifle.

"Here's a health to the Trifle,
    The tremolo Trifle,
The tremolo Trifle enveloped in cream
        As light as a dream,
        An elegant dream,
Apparel'd in cream, as light as a dream.
In spite of the liquor with which she is stored
The tottering Trifle is queen of our board.
            The Trifle,
            The Trifle,
    The Trifle so swimmy and sweet,
        In cream enclos'd
        Shall be our toast,
    With cream and cake and wine complete."

"The Trifle!" said the Prince.

"The Trifle!" cried the guests. And now it was all spoons to the mouth, and tipping of plates to secure every drop of cream and sherry wine. The Prince let fall a red glacé cherry, and the Zany caught it and popped it in his other ear, but took it out again because it made him deaf to the golden hammer that was tapping for the Pineapple.

"And last the Pineapple,
    The juicy Pineapple,
A health to the Pineapple kissed by the sun.
        It's second to none,

Exceeded by none,
Matured by the sun, it's second to none.
Each blade on its crest is as sharp as a sword,
The succulent Pine is the prince of our
         board.
                  The Pine,
                  The Pine,
         The mettlesome, pricklesome Pine,
                  Of guests and host
                  Shall be the toast,
         The fruit we taste and toast in wine."

"The Pineapple!"

"The Pineapple!" For the fourth time the glasses
were emptied. The more mannerly guests ate a few
morsels of the luscious fruit and rinsed their fingers
daintily in the bowls of scented water that had been
provided. But Arethusa and Araminta chewed their
portions right up to the edge of the prickly rind,
and shrieked because it made their lips smart, and
hastily drank from their fingerbowls, and glared at
the servingmen because it was only perfumed water
and not lemonade—"Who wants to drink scent?"
asked Araminta loudly. Meanwhile, the Prince had
passed the tallest green blade from the Pineapple
crest down to the Zany, who cut his finger on its
keen edge; but even a hurt from the master he loved

was welcome, and he thrust the blade under his tunic, where his heart could feel it.

The supper was done; yet there was one more toast to drink. The glasses were filled up with bubbling wine; the guests rose as one man and raised their glasses to the Prince, sitting among the six aristocrats with a cold, calm face that concealed the disappointment in his heart.

"LAST—" sang the Toastmaster, knocking with his hammer—

"Last a health to Prince Charming,
   Our charming Prince Charming,
A health to Prince Charming, who now is a man,
   Deny it who can,
   Dispute it who can.
No boy but a man, deny it who can.
We treasure his virtue and value his worth,
And honor his name on the day of his birth.
   Our Prince,
   Our Prince,
   Our Prince so gallant and dear,
   Shall be the toast,
   The royal toast,
Long life to our Prince, with joy and good
   cheer!"

"The Prince!" cried the gentlemen, with their voices full of zeal.

"The Prince!" echoed the ladies, with their hearts full of hope.

The Prince rose and bowed, with all hope gone from his.

CHAPTER XVI

The Prince Will Not Dance

FOLLOWED BY HIS GUESTS, the Prince returned to the ballroom, where a little orchestra of the finest musicians in the kingdom was beginning to play in an ornamental gallery above the throne. The heart of every lady present beat in time to the music; for at last the moment was approaching when the Prince would lead out his partner for the first dance—and whomever he chose would undoubtedly be his partner for life. The ladies sat round the room with their eyes modestly lowered; excepting Araminta and Arethusa, who goggled at the Prince shamelessly.

It was, however, too soon after all that supper of boar and peacock and trifle and pineapple (of which their royal host had tasted nothing) to expect the guests to dance immediately, and a little diversion had been arranged for their amusement. As the music changed from graceful to gay, into the middle of the room twirled a Harlequin, who expressed, in dumb show, how much he was consumed with love for—for whom? For an enchanting little Columbine, who now sprang lightly to twirl beside him, coquet with him, lead him on, repulse him, and twirl again. Presently, as the music became less frivolous, Columbine softened, and listened coyly while Harlequin knelt at her feet and offered her a heart of rosy silk, which he plucked out of his breast and tossed in his hands. Columbine's dainty fingers fluttered to catch it—and lo! Before she could do so the heart flew away, up, up into the glittering chandelier, and was seen no more. The guests clapped their hands; the dancers bowed and capered away in opposite directions. Had the pretty divertissement, invented for the occasion, an inner meaning—to the effect that the fair one for whom the silken heart was destined was still unknown? This was the question which all who watched the dance had asked themselves. Only the Prince did not watch. He sat sunk in his throne and in his thoughts; and under cover of the music, while all attention was attracted elsewhere, he whispered, "Zany!"

The Zany popped his head round the throne and fixed his round questioning eyes on his master.

The Prince said very sadly, "She is not here."

The Zany hung his sad head.

"She has not come."

The Zany beat his unhappy breast.

"She does not exist."

The Zany collapsed in despair.

"Yet tonight," the Prince went on, "I must make my choice. What can I do, Zany, what can I do? As each lady entered I looked at her, and listened to my heart, expectantly."

The Zany looked up, expectant.

"But each time my heart said only, 'It is not she.'"

The Zany drooped.

"'It is not she, not she.'"

The Zany lay down and died.

The Prince looked round the room, from one face to another, from one form to the next. "Every one of them is too much something, or not enough something else." The Zany came to life a little and winked at the Prince. "Get up, you Zany. What do you think you are for? I thought fools were supposed to be so wise. Why don't you help me?"

The Zany sat up on his heels and pointed to one of the ladies at random.

"Too sweet," said the Prince.

The Zany pointed to another.

"Too sour."

A third! "Too conventional." A fourth! "Too bizarre." A fifth—"Too prim-and-proper." A sixth—"Too bold-and-brazen." There was no pleasing him.

The Zany, grinning, beckoned to Arethusa. She half started from her seat.

"Ha, ha!" chuckled the Prince. "That one!"

The Zany waved Arethusa down and beckoned to Araminta.

"Ha, ha! *That* one!" The Prince chuckled again. The Zany rolled over with glee at having made him laugh.

"Hark," said the Prince. "The ladies are clapping their hands, the entertainment is over, the musicians are tuning up again, our dance is about to begin." The Zany began to dance, but the Prince stopped him. "Which one to ask? My first choice seals my fate." His eyes traveled once more round the room; wherever his glance alighted a lady breathed faster. But the royal glance came to rest on none of them. "I cannot, I will not choose!"

The musicians concluded the introduction. The ladies were now in a perfect flutter.

The Prince sprang to his feet. "Herald!" he cried.

The Herald appeared. "Your Royal Highness?" This was to be his great moment. To him, to *him* the Prince would confide his choice! His voice, *his* voice would bid that choice rejoice—

"Announce to the Court that the Prince will not be dancing."

Had the Herald's ears deceived him? "But Your Royal Highness—"

"My Royal Highness will not be dancing."

"But the lady—"

"I shall not be dancing."

The Herald made a last protest. "But the lady of your choice—where is she?"

The Prince said, "Nowhere."

"Nowhere?"

"Nowhere, nowhere, nowhere!" cried the Prince. "Announce to the guests—the lady of my choice is nowhere!"

"So be it," said the Herald in tones as wintry as the weather. He lifted a finger. A trumpeter blew a blast for silence. The Herald advanced to the center of the room.

"Ladies, attend!
An Announcement, a Pronouncement,
      a Pronunciamento!
His Highness—
His Royal Highness—
His Royal Highness the Prince—
Having inspected and reflected—
And reflected and inspected—
The selected here collected—
Desires it to be published—
Published and proclaimed—
Published and proclaimed and
      promulgated—
That the Lady—
The Lady of his Choice—
The Lady of the Prince's Choice—
Is—"

"THE PRINCESS OF NOWHERE!" boomed the
Toastmaster at the door.

CHAPTER XVII

The Princess of Nowhere

WHEN ELLA walked into the room the guests rose to their feet. At the far end, by the throne, the Prince stood transfixed. Only the Zany heard him murmur, "She is here."

"I am here," murmured Ella, floating a little farther into the room. She must be floating, it was all so dreamlike and so dazzling. Her eyes looked all around, shining with wonder; then they fell on the Prince beside his throne, and she also stood transfixed. Neither of them seemed able to move; until they did, the guests could not either. It began to look as though this would last all night.

The Herald was having to suppress a good deal of annoyance because he had not been at the door to announce the beauty of the evening; he considered that the Toastmaster had trespassed on his preserves, the Toastmaster, who, gazing after the exquisite little creature, was oozing with sentimental feelings of the most inferior kind—just like, thought the Herald, a bag of cheap pear drops melting in the sun. It was time to put a stop to all that and take things in hand. The Herald advanced as though he were preparing to dance a pavane, met Ella halfway up the floor, and made his lowest bow in his highest manner.

"Princess!"

With that one word he commanded the situation and, preceding her to the throne, presented her to the Prince as though he had just made her with his own hands. Ella managed to curtsy. The Prince managed to bow. They gazed at each other without exchanging a word.

The Prince beckoned to the Herald.

"Your Royal Highness?" said that functionary.

"Announce to the Court that the Prince would be alone."

The Herald expostulated. "But Your Royal Highness—"

"My Royal Highness would be alone."

"But the ladies—" the Herald reminded him.

"I would be alone."

"So be it."

The Herald signed to the Trumpeter, and the Trumpeter blew a blast.

"Ladies, attend!
  His Highness—
  His Royal Highness—
  His Royal Highness the Prince—
  Having meditated and cogitated,
  And cogitated and meditated
  The burning point of the turning point
  Of his existence—
  Emphatically and unenigmatically,
  And rhetorically and categorically,
  Bids all here present
  To start to depart,
  To take heed and recede,
  To be discreet and retreat
  To a considerable distance."

With a peremptory gesture the Herald swept himself and the disappointed ladies out of the room; considering himself, like everybody else, dismissed—for how could His Royal Highness possibly be *alone* if a person of his consequence remained? Having disposed the ladies in a large anteroom, he withdrew to a little one of his own, known as the Herald's Sanctum, where he sat down and sulked.

Ella, still dazed, had moved slowly away from the Prince to follow the ladies—for how could His Royal Highness be *alone* if even so little a person remained?

"Princess!" The Prince hadn't meant that at all. She turned, met his eyes again, and came back. He bowed over her hand and kissed it.

Ella said, "Oh!"

"What is the matter?"

"Nobody has ever done that before." Shyly and eagerly Ella asked, "Would you do it again?"

The Prince was puzzled. He inquired, "They do not kiss hands in Nowhere?"

"N-no," stammered Ella. "Yes. Do they?" *(Oh dear! What a muddle she was making of it.)* "I—can't remember."

"You have been so long from your native land?" asked the Prince.

"Yes. No. Have I? How stupid you must think me."

"I think you—" said the Prince, and stopped.

"What?" asked Ella.

"I cannot tell you so soon."

(Oh dear, what a pity!) "In Nowhere," Ella said, "we tell at once."

"Tell, then!" urged the Prince.

"I—I think," stammered Ella, "I think you—"

"Well?"

"I can't either." She must change the subject quickly. "What a magnificent room!"

"I suppose so," said the Prince.

"Don't you love it?"

"I think I am a little tired of it."

"I couldn't ever grow tired of it," said Ella, "unless I had to clean it."

"Clean it!" exclaimed the astonished Prince. "You!"

(*Oh dear!*) "I mean—you see—in Nowhere we do sometimes clean things ourselves. Oh yes, indeed," she assured him, gaining confidence.

"Whatever for?" asked the Prince.

She answered airily, "Different countries, different customs, you know. It never hurt anybody to know what scouring and scrubbing are." Her gaze roamed round the enormous room. "Your poor servants!" she sighed.

"Why?"

"Just think of polishing those acres of floors! Just think of shining up the throne every morning before the personages come down! And the dusting!" She stooped and ran her finger round the dais on which the Prince had been standing. "I thought so," she said, holding up her finger. "Dust under the throne!"

"It doesn't matter." The Prince wiped her finger gently with his lace handkerchief.

"It does matter." Ella shook her head.

"Don't let's talk about dusting," said the Prince. "Tell me about Nowhere. Tell me about your castles. Describe them to me. Have you many castles?"

(Oh dear!) "I—we don't have castles in Nowhere."

"What an unusual country," said the Prince. "Then tell me about your acrobats. Have you good acrobats in Nowhere?"

"We don't have acrobats," said Ella.

"No acrobats?" The Prince was surprised. He was particularly proud of his acrobats.

"No." Ella tossed her head a little. "We don't approve of them."

"I suppose it is a point of view," conceded the Prince. "How many horses do you keep?"

"We don't keep horses. But," she added with some dignity, "we have lots and lots of mice."

"How charming!" cried the Prince. "I will keep mice too. I am glad you are fond of animals. What else are you fond of? Art? People in our position should patronize art, don't you think? Have you a fine gallery in Nowhere? Do you like pictures?"

"Yes—yes, I do," stammered Ella. "I intend to get some."

"We have many fine pictures." The Prince took her hand and led her round the room, pointing out the priceless paintings on the walls. "That is a picture of my great-great-grandmother."

"What lovely green hair!" said Ella admiringly.

"She was a water nymph," remarked the Prince. "In one of the best rivers, of course. And this is my grand-grand-great-uncle."

Ella considered the picture, and then she considered the Prince. "You aren't very like him."

"No," he agreed.

"I'm glad," said Ella.

"He couldn't help having two noses," said the Prince. "He offended a witch."

"Poor man," sighed Ella.

"Poor man," sighed the Prince. He pressed her hand to comfort her as they gazed at the grand-grand-great-uncle's two noses.

"What did he do to offend the witch?" asked Ella.

"He cut off her nose," said the Prince.

"Poor witch," sighed Ella.

"Poor witch," sighed the Prince.

They came a little closer to each other in their sorrow for the witch.

"What is the time?" asked Ella suddenly.

"Who cares?" said the Prince.

But Ella cared a great deal. "What *is* the time?" she entreated.

"Ten minutes past eleven."

Ella shut her eyes and tried to count. "How many seconds in fifty minutes?"

"Three thousand—why?" asked the Prince.

She did not tell him why. "Three thousand," she murmured.

"And alas, time flies," said the Prince. "I must attend to my guests."

"Must you?" said Ella wistfully.

"Forgive me, I must," he said gently. He struck a little bell that rang in the Herald's Sanctum. The Herald appeared instantly.

"Your Royal Highness?"

"It is ten minutes past eleven—"

"So be it," said the Herald stiffly. Was it *his* fault?

"Summon the ladies," commanded the Prince. "Let the dancing begin."

"So be it," said the Herald, not quite so stiffly; but as he passed out of the room his shoulders managed to suggest that it was high time indeed.

But Ella wished the dancing might be put off forever. She remembered, from very long ago, the party when she was a little child, and they had all danced, as children dance, without thinking, for delight, and afterward they played gay games. The dancing children had not been taught how to dance, nor had Ella, then or later. She would have had dancing lessons, no doubt, if her mother had lived; and no doubt the mothers of all these pretty, well-mannered girls, these countesses and duchesses and margravines, had seen to it for them. Oh dear, oh dear, oh dear!

She said rather tremulously, "The ladies are very accomplished?"

"Accomplished? No doubt, in their way."

"The ladies will have been taught dancing?"

"Presumably."

Ella plucked up her courage to tell him, "We are not taught dancing in Nowhere."

"I am sure," smiled the Prince, "you have no need to be."

"We do not dance very well in Nowhere," she faltered.

"You are too modest," said the Prince.

"I'm not, I'm not!"

"Nevertheless," he said, "you will be my partner?"

"Yes," said Ella, "I will be your partner. Will you do something for me?"

"Anything you ask."

She held her hand toward him. "Kiss my hand again." The Prince kissed it. "Thank you."

"Aren't you a funny girl!" She puzzled him so.

"Not very," whispered Ella.

They looked at each other, finding no more to say.

"Way for the ladies!" the Herald called outside.

CHAPTER XVIII

How They Dance in Nowhere

THE LADIES had been on the tiptoe of curiosity while they waited, asking themselves and one another a thousand questions. Why had the Prince desired to be alone with the beautiful little newcomer from Nowhere? Was he smitten? Wasn't he smitten? Could he help being smitten? Wasn't she by far the most exquisite little lady ever seen in the kingdom? Where did she come from? Where did she get the material for that dress? Who was her dressmaker? What was he saying to her now? Back tripped the ladies to the ballroom, all agog. The Herald rounded them up like a flock of sheep.

"Ladies in a circle!" he commanded, as the musicians struck up for the first dance. The ladies, all obedience, formed themselves into a ring in the middle of the floor. "The ladies," announced the Herald, "will wait until the Prince has opened the ball with the first measure." The ladies' hearts fluttered like aspen leaves. Each one was thinking: *Suppose, after all, he opens the ball with me? . . .* But the Prince was bowing to the Princess of Nowhere, and the aspen leaves stopped fluttering.

Ella was whispering, "Do we have to start it?" The Prince bowed again. "Oh dear!" she whispered.

He led her into the center of the circle, where she stood like a bewildered child; all eyes were fixed on her, waiting for her first movement, and the music sparkled in her ears. The music! Why—it was the very tune her mother had played for the children at the party. Ella clapped her hands and, without thinking twice, broke into a joyous dance, as light, as funny, as unconscious as a child. It was easy! You didn't have to learn this sort of dance; you just danced! The musicians played eight bars and reached a pause; Ella, with flushed cheeks, stopped too in front of the Prince, asking merrily, "Like that?"

Behind her the ladies were murmuring that it

was highly peculiar, not like anything *they* had ever been taught in the classes of Monsieur Piff-Paff-Pouff or Madame Point-de-Pied. They were not at all sure that they knew how to do it. But the Prince was gazing at Ella as though he had never seen dancing so charming before, and this gave her confidence to turn to the ladies and say lightly, "That happens to be how we dance in Nowhere."

"That happens to be how they dance in Nowhere," the ladies explained to one another. They would just have to try, that was all. When the musicians repeated the tune they picked up their skirts and fell to dancing like children. Ella continued to cut her funny little capers, full of glee; and the ladies continued to follow suit, becoming all the time a little gayer, a little younger, a little more mindful of what fun it was to be a child at a party!

When the music stopped they were all panting and laughing and hoping they hadn't disgraced themselves. The Herald's eyes said plainly that such romps were quite inadmissible, wholly unpermissible, and should never be visible at a royal ball. Pooh! What did the Herald matter? Hadn't the Prince himself romped like a schoolboy? As for what *he* thought of the ladies, he hadn't even seen them; he had eyes only for the Princess of Nowhere, who was standing beside him and fanning herself while she recovered her breath.

Now she was laying her fingers on his wrist and saying, "I shall take your arm and walk a little."

And he was asking tenderly, "You are tired?"

"Me?" cried Ella. "I could dance till—till midnight. But I have a fancy to meet your guests."

"If only there were no guests!" whispered the Prince.

"It wouldn't be a party without guests," she said.

She began to parade the room on the Prince's arm, saying, "Good evening!" sweetly to the Countess of Caraway. The Countess sank to the floor in a deep curtsy. "What fun!" cried Ella. "Good evening! Good evening! Good evening!" One after another the ladies went down before her, falling and rising like rainbow waves as she passed. To think that all these grand strangers were eager for her notice, that her word or her smile could bow them to the ground. What fun! If only they knew!

Now she was coming to the three who knew her too well. Would the Fairy's spell hold, or would the Sisters and the Stepmother see through it? No, they were craning forward, with no sign of recognition, as greedy for her notice as all the others.

"Good evening," she said with special graciousness.

Arethusa and Araminta dip-dip-dipped. The Stepmother kissed the hand of the Princess of Nowhere. Ella's eyes sparkled—oh! She *was* having fun.

"There now, Arethusa," she exclaimed, "your feather is crooked again."

"Your Highness knows my daughter's name?" stammered the Stepmother.

"In Nowhere," the Princess explained, after thinking a moment, "we know everybody's name—by instinct. Your beauty spot should be on the *other* cheek, Araminta!"

"Miraculous instinct!" gasped the Stepmother.

"I never did see such instinction," said Arethusa.

With a touch here and a touch there, the Princess graciously straightened Thusa's feather and changed Minta's patch.

"Such condescension," murmured the Stepmother. They dip-dip-dipped again as the Princess passed on.

But the Prince had had enough of the parade. "Come away," he said under his breath. "You are wasting your time."

"My time!" Ella clasped her hands, as though

she could hold time in them and stop it. "What time is it?" she asked.

"It is half-past eleven."

She shut her eyes and counted. "Eighteen hundred seconds. Quick, quick, let's dance again. Oh, *I* know—let's play a game."

"The company will play a game," said the Prince to the Herald.

"The Company will play a Game!" proclaimed the Herald. "What game," he asked icily, "will the company play?"

"Hide-and-seek," said Ella promptly. (That was the party game so long ago.)

"Hide-and-Seek!" announced the Herald. "Hide-and-Seek."

"They must shut their eyes," said Ella, remembering.

"Shut Your Eyes," pronounced the Herald. "Shut Your Eyes!"

All eyes were instantly shut.

"They must give me time till I count three," said Ella.

"Give Her Time," decreed the Herald, without opening his eyes, "Till She Counts Three."

They were all ears to hear which way she ran; but she ran so lightly that they heard no sound until her clear voice called, *"One!"* not very far away.

"Two!" Still clear, but distant. *"Three!"* More distant still. And then, farther than ever: *"Come and find me. Where am I?"*

"Where Is She?" demanded the Herald, opening his eyes.

"Where is she?" echoed the ladies, opening theirs. They began wandering about, looking for the Princess of Nowhere, who was nowhere to be seen. Hither and thither they ran, playing the delicious, mysterious game of hide-and-seek.

But to the Prince her going was not a game. He hunted feverishly, crying, "Where is she? Where is she?" Oh, if only he had not played fair and had peeped through his eyelids. But princes, there's no help for it, have to play fair.

Ah, but zanies are zanies and don't know the rules of fair play. The Zany had played half-fair and closed one eye, but kept the other open like a cat when it is pretending to sleep; and he had seen the Princess tiptoe out of the room. He pulled at the Prince's cloak, and pointed to the right—then, leaping among the ladies, he led them away to the left.

The Prince ran quickly, quickly to the Orangery.

CHAPTER XIX

"Where Are You?"

"WHERE ARE YOU?" called the ladies in the distance. "Where is the Princess? Where are you?"

"I knew you would find me," said Ella. "I think I knew you would." She was standing under one of the orange trees, not trying to hide at all. The Prince came and stood beside her. "How quick you were," said Ella. "How did you know I would be here?"

The Prince was too honorable to give the Zany away. He said, smiling, "You say you know everybody's name by instinct. Perhaps you are not the only clever one. Perhaps I know where everybody is by instinct."

"You are making fun of me," said Ella. "But it doesn't matter. As long as you knew where I was—that's all that matters."

"Yes," he said, "that's all I care about now—always to know where you are, where you are today, where you were yesterday, where you will be to-morrow."

"Don't let's talk about tomorrow," she begged. "Hateful tomorrow!"

"But tomorrow is always so exciting," said the Prince.

"Is it?"

"There is so much to do."

"Oh yes, so much! That's true."

"Why did you sigh?"

"Did I? I'm happy really. I've never been so happy. I shall never be so happy again."

"What a mystery you are!" said the Prince. "You were made for joy, yet there is a tear in your heart. Why is it?"

Ella looked round at the white and gold and green of the orange trees in the delicate glass room. "How beautiful it is here!"

"What is your secret?" asked the Prince.

"I have never seen such a wonderful place!"

"You would rather not speak about yourself."

"I would rather speak about you. Are you very, very happy?"

"Sometimes," he said, "I am extraordinarily happy, and yet I haven't the faintest notion why. And sometimes I am extraordinarily unhappy, and I don't know why either."

"How strange!" said Ella. "It is exactly the same with me."

"That is very remarkable. Tell me something else about yourself."

"What shall I tell you?"

"Anything. What do you want?"

"So many things." She thought a moment. "I want to be good, for one thing. I try to be good, I do try, and to like everybody. But there are some people—some people I *can't* like, however much I try. I hate them—there!"

"But it is amazing!" exclaimed the Prince.

"What?"

"I am just like that too. We seem to have a good deal in common. Do you like getting up in the morning?"

"Oh no-o-o-o-!"

"Nor I! That must be more than coincidence. Are you fond of flowers?"

"I adore them!"

"So do I," said the Prince. "We might have been made for each other."

Far away in the distance the voices were faintly calling, "Where are you? Where is she? Where is the Princess?" He saw her shrink.

"Do you hope the others won't find us?"

"It is at the back of my mind all the time," said Ella.

"And it is at the back of mine."

She looked at him earnestly, saying, "Let us have one moment we shall never forget."

"I shall never forget any of these moments."

"But let us have one special moment. Always, always to remember. Take my hand."

He took it. "Yes?"

"Now!" Ella gazed at him still more earnestly. "This is the moment we shall never forget. Say it with me."

"Am I really here?" she asked. "Is it really me?"

"Yes, darling, yes. Of course it is really you."

"It is all so queer. So much has happened. I want to be sure." Again she looked at him with wondering eyes. "I'm not dreaming?"

"Your eyes are wide, wide awake," he promised her.

"And that is you?"

He smiled and said, "I hope so."

"I hope so too! . . . Did you call me darling just now?"

"Did you hear me?"

"I heard you, but did you?"

"Shall I say it again?"

"No," she said quickly, "no! Once is better than twice, once is better than twice. I shall tell myself that all the rest of my life—once is better than— What is the time?" she asked suddenly.

"Always the time. A quarter to twelve, funny."

She shook her head. "Not funny, not funny."

Outside, a little nearer, she could hear them (*"Where is she? Where are you?"*), and she caught her breath.

The Prince said, "They are coming."

"Yes."

"Let us go outside."

"In the snow?"

"Yes."

"Yes!"

"Take my hand again."

He held out his, and she took it, saying, "The moon will look lovely on the snow. How lovely it is when everything is lovely."

"Where are you?" called the ladies at the door. They opened it and peeped into the Orangery, but she was not there, only a little wind was blowing a drift of snow through an open window.

CHAPTER XX

Cream Tarts and Sugarplums

THE FATHER stood in the crunchy snow on the terrace, sheltering in an angle by a window. He shivered a little, because his old suit really had worn very thin, but no one would notice him in this shadowy corner. He had taken no part in the festivities. In the ballroom he had been pushed aside by Arethusa and Araminta, who were ashamed of the shabby figure he cut. At the supper table the Stepmother had grabbed the best dishes that were presented to them, and emptied his glass of wine as well as her own. But he didn't mind—his thoughts were all on Ella. The Fairy's magic had deprived him, like everybody else, of the power to recognize his little daughter in the Princess of Nowhere; and he imagined her sitting alone in the dark kitchen, waiting for him to come back from the ball and tell her all about it—*"Everything,"* she had insisted, "Every speck!" The questions she would ask! But oh dear, his poor old memory! He tapped his forehead, counting over the things he must try to remember.

"Let's see. The curtains are lined with cloth of silver. The Toastmaster has gold frogs on his coat. The chandeliers carry five hundred candles apiece. The ceiling is painted with stars and flying cupids. The dancing floor is as smooth and as bright as ice. Arethusa fell down twice on it. The ladies wore all the colors of the rainbow. The Prince— the Prince—bless me if I can remember a single thing about the Prince. Tut! My poor mind, my poor mind!" He peered through the window, trying to see the Prince. But there wasn't a sign of him; the ladies were all alone. How disappointed Ella would be if he couldn't remember the Prince.

To comfort himself, he stopped counting his thoughts and fumbled in his deep pockets to count the goodies he had hidden inside them. He had managed to sneak a few from the supper table before it was cleared, and now he drew them out, like a miser counting his hoard. Seven almonds, a bunch of raisins, and a candied orange. *She'll like those; she'll be pleased with those,* thought the Father, and wished there were more of them. And so there would have been; but while he was sneaking the goodies into his pocket he had seen that queer Zany staring at him with round eyes, and he had slipped outside before the fellow could tell on him. After all, it *wasn't* the way to behave at a party.

And now—dear, dear! Here came the Zany himself, padding round the corner as softly as a cat. He had a plate in his hand. Was he going to demand the almonds and raisins back? Would he make the Father give up the candied orange?

No! He was holding out the pretty plate with a cunning look in his round eyes. On the plate was a handful of bonbons in gold and silver paper.

"For me?" asked the Father.

The Zany shook his head.

"For Ella?"

The Zany nodded.

"You knew I had a little girl at home? And perhaps you remember what it was like to be a child and left out of things."

The Zany sighed heavily, remembering what it was like to be left out. He tipped the bonbons into the Father's pocket, and ran away. Well, who would have thought it! The Father had a friend at Court! He counted the bonbons joyfully—there were nine of them! How Ella would enjoy them.

The Zany reappeared with a dish full of sugarplums, which he poured into the Father's hands, and ran away again. The Father counted them. Fifteen exquisite sugarplums, of different colors! So the Father hadn't come to the ball for nothing—nobody could say *that* about him now.

Just as he tucked the fifteenth sugarplum away, the Zany stole back for the third time, carrying a cake basket. He offered it to the Father, his round eyes rounder then ever.

"Ah, my simple friend, something more for my little daughter? What is it this time?"

It was twelve cream tarts. The Father scratched his head.

"They will be rather difficult to conceal on my person. It is a pity—she would like them so much."

The Zany wiped away a tear for the pity of it.

"All the same, it is more than kind of you."

The Zany was cheered up by his more than kindness.

"But what can be done with them?"

The Zany knew! He ate one—with pleasure; a second—with ecstasy; a third—oh, rapture! He crammed the remaining nine into his mouth so rapidly that one tripped over the other and covered his chin with cream, while his eyes goggled.

"Ha, ha, what a child you are!" chuckled the Father. "A perfect baby."

The Zany sucked his thumb like a perfect baby.

"Yet when I was telling you about my little Ella, I should have said you were a sage, far gone in years."

The Zany tottered on his feet like a little old man, his eyes as round and wise as any owl's—and suddenly toppled head over heels in a somersault. One really never knew where to have him next!

When he came right end up he put his finger to his lips and cocked his ear. At the far end of the terrace the Prince was leading his Princess out of the Orangery very secretly.

Very secretly the Zany led the Father away, out of sight. They crept like two boys going to steal apples.

CHAPTER XXI

Ladies in the Snow

THE SNOW had gone to everybody's heads. The golden palace was deserted for the silver garden. Such a thing had never happened at a royal ball before. Ceremony had been cast aside; etiquette had flown to the winds. The musicians, with nobody to hear them, played dance music with nobody to dance to it. The Toastmaster had nobody to toast. The Herald no guests to command to do this or do that. All the rules were being broken. His authority was being flouted, routed, could one dare to say doubted? It was unthinkable, unpardonable, and unbearable that the ladies should be so utterly don'tcareable. He fussed hither and thither, trying to find a few of them, at least, say, two of them—even one, rather than none of them would do. Was one too much to ask?

It was. They had all wandered away into the spellbound, moonstruck, snow-enchanted garden. For what, forsooth? To play at hide-and-seek! Their distant voices floated, light as snowflakes, from all quarters:

> *"Where are you?*
> *Where is the Princess?*
> *Where are you?"*

The voices called in vain. The Princess of Nowhere bore a charmed life. She and the Prince, moving as though invisible here or there, continued to tell each other all about themselves, in a world of their own.

Once when the calling voices sounded like elf horns faintly in the distance, the Prince covered her with his mantle, whispering, "They shall never find you."

"What fun!" whispered Ella.

They forgot the ladies and went on telling.

Once they lingered by the window to a little anteroom, where the Father was helping himself furtively to something on a table. The Prince whispered, "The old gentleman is putting walnuts into his pocket. He looks rather guilty."

"No, he is very innocent," whispered Ella. "Walnuts! How sweet of him."

"I don't see why," whispered the Prince.

They forgot the old gentleman and went on telling.

Once they almost ran into Minta and Thusa, who were seeking not for the Princess of Nowhere but for the Prince. The Zany slipped up behind him just in time, twitched off his mantle, and skipped away in it. The Prince went on with Ella, noticing nothing, while the Zany trailed the mantle along the snow and Minta and Thusa ran after it like kittens, crying, "Dear Prince! Stop, Prince! Sweet Prince! Stay!" Every now and then he stood on his head, and, when they had all but caught him, turned a cartwheel and was off again. The Sisters panted after the royal mantle, but never caught a glimpse of the wearer's face.

Now from every glade and grove and dingle in the grounds, from every bush glittering with rime and every little tree tinkling with icicles, the voices of the ladies in the snow came in soft chorus as they tiptoed to and fro, catching one another, but never the one they sought.

"Princess, where are you?
Where are you? . . .
Hiding, seeking,
Seeking, hiding,
Peeping, creeping,
And colliding,
Is that she?
Is that she?
No! No!
It's only a tree,
Only a tree,
In the snow.
Make no sound,
Step very light
On the ground
Glimmering white—
If she is near us
She mustn't hear us,
She mustn't hear us,
Must not, must not
Hear us. . . .
Here! Here!
Come over here!
Can it be she?
Follow me. . . .
Found! Found!

Can it be true?
Oh dear!
Is it only you?
Only, only
You!—
There! There!
Look over there!
Soft as you can!
Don't make a stir!
That's her fan!
That's her fur!
Caught! Caught!
Oh dear!
Is it only her?
It is only, only
Her. . . .
Make no noise!
Step like a bird!
Pause and poise
Lest you be heard!
Should she be near us
She mustn't hear us,
She mustn't hear us,
Must not, must not
Hear us. . . .
List'ning,
Looking,

Looking,
List'ning,
Something
Gleaming,
Something
Glist'ning!
Is that she?
Is that she?
No! No!
It's a tree,
A tree,
Only a tree,
Only a tree
In the snow.

"Where are you?" called the ladies, very clear.
Large flakes of snow were falling on the night.
The Herald appeared from the main entrance
on the terrace to announce:

"The ladies will return to the ballroom
    For the minuet!"
"Not yet! Not yet!" *(called the ladies).*
"Their Majesties are apprehensive lest
    the ladies
    Should get wet!" *(announced the
    Herald).*
"Not yet! Not yet!" *(they pouted).*

"The presence of the ladies is absolutely
  imperative
  To make up the set!" *(insisted the
  Herald)*.
"Not yet! Not yet!" *(they pleaded)*.
"Nevertheless by Royal command
  THE LADIES WILL NOW RETURN TO
THE BALLROOM FOR—THE—MINUET!"

Light as snowflakes, the ladies returned to the
ballroom.

CHAPTER XXII

"Twelve O'clock!"

THE GARDENS were deserted. Only the Prince and Ella continued to stroll and whisper on the terrace, where the snow was dotted with the heel-and-toe marks of the ladies' dancing shoes. Now, behind the lighted windows of the ballroom, they were dancing the minuet to sweet strains from the musicians' gallery. The music mingled with the moonlight and became part of the dream in which Ella seemed to be floating.

She said to the Prince, "We should be dancing."

"Yes."

"But we are not dancing."

"No. Shall we go in?"

"I would rather stay out here. It is such a beautiful dream."

Into the music of the dream came a new note. *"Tweet-tweet!"* But she did not hear it. Overhead the clock on the Palace front was ticking louder, *"Tick-tock! Tick-tock!"* in a voice very like Grandpa's. But she did not notice.

The Prince was saying, "And still—"

"Still?"

"Still I have not told you—"

"Told me?"

"How much—how very much—" said the Prince.

"I don't think you need to tell me," whispered Ella. She added shyly, "But perhaps it would do no harm."

She stood still while he told her.

"Tick-tock!" said the clock overhead. *"The time! Remember the time!"*

Oh yes, she would remember the time! The Prince was still whispering in her ear, and she knew that this was the time she would always remember, the time she would never let go as she sat in the cinders and watched the ashes glowing on the hearth. . . . The Prince was still whispering. . . .

Yes, this was *her* time, nobody's time but hers, no matter what happened ever after, no matter if she were sad, or tired, or frightened, she would never be lonely as she used to be. . . . He went on whispering. . . . Oh, if only make-believing didn't have to come to an end, if only dreams were as true as truth, and truth as dreamy as dreams! I wish, she thought, I wish . . . I wish this night were forever! I wish wishing made it come true! I wish it would go on forever and ever and ever and ever and—

"ONE!" boomed the clock.

Ella started, her eyes big, like a child waking up.

"TWO!"

She must go!

"THREE!"

The dream was over, she must go. . . .

"Princess!" The Prince caught her hand, startled because she looked so startled—

"FOUR!"

"Let me go, let me go!" cried Ella, and began to run.

"FIVE!"

He was running after her—where could she go, where could she hide, before he discovered that she was not a princess anymore, only the little girl who sifted the cinders?

"SIX! SEVEN!" boomed the clock.

The minuet had stopped; the ladies were flocking out to the terrace again, calling, "Where are you? Where are you?"

"EIGHT!"

They had seen her! They were surrounding her, crying, "Caught! Caught! Caught!" She ran from side to side, trying to escape. The Prince was running after her, the ladies were closing in.

"NINE! TEN! ELEVEN!"

Now she was in their midst, so close pressed that she could no longer be seen. The Prince, distracted, was trying to force his way in, to rescue his little Princess from the laughing, teasing ladies, and to tell them aloud what he had whispered in her ear, that this was the lady of his heart, his chosen bride, that he would marry her tomorrow—

"TWELVE!"

Out of the struggling throng ran a small shabby girl in rags, with cinders in her hair and ashes on her hands. The ladies did not even notice her; they were looking for someone else. The Prince saw the flying form of a girl brush by him, a girl who was not the Princess of Nowhere; he thrust her aside, crying, "Out of my way!" and sent her tumbling down the steps. The ladies opened out, to uncover the lovely creature they had caught like a butterfly, who must be there among them. But there was not a sign of her.

"Where are you?" they called. "Where are you?"

"Where is she?" cried the Prince to the air, in vain. The Princess of Nowhere was nowhere.

The Zany scrambled up the slippery steps, hugging something to his breast. He fell on his knees before the Prince, and laid at his feet the precious thing he had found at the foot of the stairs.

It was a glass slipper.

CHAPTER XXIII

"I Knew It Wasn't True"

OUTSIDE THE KITCHEN, in the falling snow, the Rooster crowed, *"Cockadoodledoo!"*

Inside the kitchen, in her narrow bed, Ella stirred and murmured, "Not funny . . . not very . . . "

All round the room the voices of the Things began their effort to wake her up in time.

"The grandfather clock agrees with the cock," ticked the Clock.

"They mustn't find us, they mustn't ever find us," murmured Ella.

"Make haste with the mop, the mop and the slop," dripped the Tap.

"We should be dancing . . . " murmured Ella.

"The grime in the room could do with a groom," bumped the Broom.

But Ella only turned over, murmuring, "This is the moment we shall never forget."

"*Cockadoodledoo!*" crowed the Rooster in the snow.

"It's no good, Rooster," said the Clock. "She's dreaming too deep. *You've* crowed and crowed. *I've* ticked and tocked. She won't wake up till she wants to wake up—what do you say, Rocking Chair?"

"That's what comes of keeping late hours," creaked the Rocking Chair. "What do you say, Broom?"

"Young and scatterbrained," said the Broom. "She'll only get scolded, and serve her right."

"She'll only get scolded, and serve her right," echoed the Things on all sides. But on the mantelpiece the little musical box began to tinkle sweetly; and Ella, on her bed, murmured with her eyes shut, "That's how we happen to dance in Nowhere . . . we do, we *do*. . . . "

A tremendous knocking on the front door shook the house.

"There's the family come home," said the Clock. "Now she'll catch it."

The knocking was repeated furiously.

"Wake up! Wake up! Wake up! Now you'll catch it! Wake up! Wake up!" cried the Things.

The knocking stopped, and the sudden silence did what all the noise had failed to. Ella sat up in bed and rubbed her eyes.

"Oh dear!" She stretched her arms. "Was it a dream, then?" She gazed round the room at the familiar Things. "Goodness, look at the Clock! Hurry, Ella, hurry!" She tumbled out of bed in her rags, just as she had tumbled into it a few hours ago, and scurried here and there, trying to make up for lost time. "Lazybones!" she scolded herself. "Dreaming. . . . I knew it wasn't true, I knew it wasn't . . . "

Bang! Bang! Thump! But now it was the back door that rattled.

"Open the door, open the door!" banged Arethusa and Araminta. "Open the door this instant!" thumped the Stepmother.

"Oh *dear!*" whispered Ella.

She pulled back the bolts, and the three trailed in, cold with the frost, draggled with the slush, fractious with the lateness of the hour, and thoroughly exhausted.

"So we're to freeze to death on the doorstep, are we?" demanded the Stepmother. "Knock till Doomsday, can we? Traipse down to the back door, must we? And all because my fine lady, fresh from a good night's sleep, won't answer the front door, won't she?" The angry woman's tirade was interrupted by a long yawn. She flopped into a chair, groaning, "I'm fit to drop."

Arethusa flopped onto another, muttering, "What about me? My ankles are all swelled up like nothing on earth."

Araminta followed suit, complaining, "I can't hardly feel my feet, they're that puffed up."

"I *can* hardly feel my feet," corrected the Stepmother.

"But I *can't*, Ma," whined Araminta.

"When you've quite done arguing," snapped the Stepmother, "perhaps this young lady will condescend to take off our boots."

"Me first! Me first!" squealed the Sisters.

"You next!" glared the Stepmother, thrusting out her feet. Ella knelt down, and while she began to draw off the heavy snowboots she asked timidly, "Then there really *was*—a ball?"

"Ow!" said the Stepmother as the first boot came away. "*Was* a ball, child? Where do you think we've been all night? Of course there was a ball."

"Of course," agreed Ella eagerly. She pulled off the second boot. "Was it a nice ball?"

"Ow!" said the Stepmother. "It was a dream

of a ball," she mumbled through a yawn.

Ella's face fell. "A dream?"

"Rub my feet," said the Stepmother. "Harder! Not so hard! Softer! Not so soft . . . " She fell asleep as suddenly as a cat when it is bored with being awake.

"Cinders!" yawned Arethusa, sticking her feet out.

Ella hastened across to ease the boots off. "Were your dresses much admired?" she asked.

"Admired!" simpered Arethusa. "They were the talk of the supper table. Brrrr! My tootsies are lumps of ice—go on! Rub-a-dub-dub!"

Ella rubbed away at the enormous tootsies diligently. "Was it a very grand supper?" Everything she could learn would help a little.

"Grand is no word for it!" said Arethusa greedily. "What you missed! Helpings and helpings of peacock! Mountains and mountains of trifle! And more boar—you never saw more boar!"

"And as for the Prince!" simpered Araminta.

In a moment Ella was at Minta's feet. "What about the Prince? What about him?" she implored, tugging at the third pair of boots.

"Talk about larks!" tittered Araminta.

"He was all over us!" giggled Arethusa.

Ella stared. (It couldn't be true, then!)

"We danced with him!" said Arethusa.

"We sang with him!" said Araminta.

"We flirted with him!"

"*The* most delightful man!"

"And comical! You never saw anything like it! He walked on his hands and turned head over heels for us."

"Head over heels, Thusy?"

"Of course."

"Whatever for?"

"Just his blue blood, I suppose," shrugged Arethusa.

Araminta added, "To show he was head over heels in love with us."

"The *Prince*?" said Ella wonderingly.

"Do you suggest," asked Minta, "we're telling tarradiddles?"

"Oh no, only—I dreamed about a Prince," murmured Ella, "and he didn't turn head over heels."

"Dreams go by contraries, my girl," yawned Araminta. "I thought any fool knew that. Eee-yah! Don't Ma look a sight?"

The Stepmother was snoring with her mouth wide open, and her wig askew on her bald head.

"Eee-yah!" nodded Arethusa. "You'd better

see to the fire, Cinders, or she'll give you beans when she wakes up. P'raps you like beans. Eee-yah!"

"Eeee-yah!" yawned Araminta.

And they dropped off as suddenly as the Stepmother had done. Poor Ella crept over to the hearth and began sadly to make up the fire. If that was the ball her stepsisters had gone to, the one she remembered *must* have been a dream. Oh dear! She knew it wasn't true. Oh dear . . .

CHAPTER XXIV

A Sugarplum for Ella

SOMETHING DROPPED OVER her shoulder into her lap. It was a sugarplum.

She looked round quickly. Her Father was standing behind her, his finger to his lips. He had been lingering outside the window, waiting for the three ladies to go upstairs, for he wanted to catch Ella by herself. It was with great disappointment that he had seen the three drop one by one into the chairs, and yawn and jabber and yawn and fall asleep. Now they were all snoring so loud that they couldn't possibly hear the door open; and he took his chance to slip in and comfort his little daughter, crouched on the hearth at the other side of the room. He sat down on a stool, and she knelt beside him, turning her sugarplum in the firelight to make it sparkle a little.

"Tell me!" she whispered. "Tell me!"

He glanced round cautiously at the three snorers. "What shall I tell you?"

"Everything!"

He scratched his head and tried to cudgel his brains.

"*Everything*, Father!"

"Well—" he began, and stopped.

"Go on," she whispered. She would have to help him. "Did they announce your name at the door, and did you go in?"

"Oh yes, I went right in, yes, all the way in."

"And was it very gay and grand and bright?"

"You'd never believe how grand and bright it was."

"And were there lots and lots of pretty ladies?"

"Pretty enough," said the Father, "pretty enough."

"Who was the prettiest?"

He wagged his sly old head. "It wasn't Thusa, my dear."

"No?"

"And it wasn't Minta, my dear."

"No?"

"But after supper," whispered the Father, smiling, "such a supper, Ella!—when we thought everybody had arrived, the duchesses, the countesses, the margravines, and all that—the doors were flung open—there was a sudden buzz—a flourish of trumpets—and in came the Princess of Nowhere."

"*What?*" Ella clasped her hands tight under her chin.

"The Princess of Nowhere."

"Say it again!" she cried—still in a whisper.

"The Princess of Nowhere."

"Then it *is* true!" She sprang to her feet in a transport of joy. "It *wasn't* a dream!"

"Of course it's true!" said the Father.

"True, true, true!" sang Ella, dancing round him. "It's true, true, true!"

"Sh! Sh! Sh!" whispered the Father.

"sh! sh! sh!" whispered Ella very loud, at the three snoring ladies. She dropped on her knees again beside the Father. "And was *she* the prettiest?"

"Much the prettiest." He nodded.

"The prettiest you ever saw?" she urged.

He shook his head. "I may be an old silly, but you know, Ella, you yourself have always seemed to me—"

"Oh no, Father! Not as pretty as the Princess from Nowhere. The Princess *was* the prettiest you ever saw—say it, Father!—wasn't she?"

He confessed reluctantly, "The Princess was the prettiest I ever saw."

"Oh, Father!" She hugged him. How her heart was beating! "And the Prince—what did the Prince do?"

"He never took his eyes off her."

"Oh, Father! And her dress?"

"Her dress?" He had to scratch his head again. "Let me see—it was all— I'm not much of a hand at describing dresses, Ella, but—yes, it was just such a dress as I should like to be able to give you— that describes it exactly—just such a dress as I should like to give you. And all I have to give you is a sugarplum."

Her arms stole round his neck. "Oh, Father— you have given me more than that."

CHAPTER XXV

The Glass Slipper

AN ALARUM OF TRUMPETS woke the three snorers with a start. They sat up, crying, "Good gracious!" and the Stepmother sat up so suddenly that her wig fell off. Nobody knew till this moment that she hadn't a hair on her head, and as she went to bed in her wig she had forgotten it herself. The Herald's red and gold flashed past the window. The Sisters rubbed their knuckles in their eyes, muttering, "It can't be another ball!" and the Stepmother groped to recover her wig before it was too late; but she was still as bald as an egg when the door burst open and the Herald, followed by the Trum-

167

peter and the Footman, stood bowing before her.

"Ladies!" He made his most elegant flourish.

"Sir!" The Sisters made their clumsiest curtsies in their disarray.

The Stepmother, deeply embarrassed, began to babble, "You find us—as it were—once again—as it were—very much—as it were—"

The Herald turned his head away from the sorry sight she presented. "Say no more. Courtesy averts an eye. Good manners are myopic. Permit me." Stooping for the wig, he presented it to her with his back turned.

"I am covered, sir, with confusion," said the Stepmother, putting it on.

"That you should be covered with anything, madam, is a matter for universal rejoicing," said the Herald.

"Sir!" curtsied the ladies.

The Herald waved a peremptory hand, closing the incident. "Dalliance delays. Duty demands. Once again I come from His Royal Highness the Prince on a mission, a commission, a charge, an errand, an embassy—"

"To us?" asked the delighted Sisters.

"The Prince," joined in the Stepmother, "sends you to *us*?"

"The Prince, ladies, has deputed me to announce his inviolable, unimpeachable, immovable, irreprovable, immutable, and most suitable choice— of a Bride."

"It's me!" crowed Arethusa, going as purple as a beetroot.

" 'Tisn't, it's me!" Araminta went as red-and-white as radishes.

The Stepmother, dizzy with pride, did her best to live up to the occasion. "You come, sir, to announce this auspicious, this delicious, and, if I may say so, this highly propitious news to *us*?"

"To you, to you, ladies!" fluted the Herald. "Ladies, ladies, to you!"

"I'm all of a tremble," said Arethusa. "Which one of us is it?"

The Herald raised his hand. "Eschew prematurity."

"What does *that* mean?" asked Araminta. "Me or Thusy?"

"I will be plain." The Herald signed to the Footman to deliver a scroll, from which he read in his most polished diction:

"Proclaim it far! Proclaim it wide!
Let one and all be notified,
With pride and pomp, and pomp and pride,
The Prince has chosen for his bride,

His fate, his mate, his nuptial guide,
In wedded bliss to be allied,
Whoever, when this shoe is tried,
Can get both toe and heel inside."

The Footman stepped forward and presented a cushion covered with cloth of gold, on which reposed a slipper made of glass, the very tiniest slipper ever seen.

"Let me look! Let me look!" Ella darted from the back of the kitchen with flushed cheeks and sparkling eyes. Now there could be no doubt that it was true!

The Stepmother slapped at her, saying sharply, "Cinders!"

"Oh, get out of my *way*!" cried the excited child, pushing the Stepmother aside.

"How *dare* you!" she thundered, and slapped again, leaving one of Ella's cheeks redder than the other.

The Herald stepped between them. "Young person," he said to Ella, "your chance will come in its appointed turn."

"*Her* chance!" protested the wrathful Stepmother.

The Herald said coldly, "The Prince's decree

covers every unmarried female in the land."

"Do you mean to say," pouted Arethusa, "he didn't send you special to us?"

The Herald began, "He sent me special to—" stopped short, and went on icily, "The Prince sent me *especially* to everybody. All at the ball are bidden to bring their toes to the trial. Whom the shoe fits, let her wear it."

"Hide those boots!" hissed the Stepmother in the Father's ear.

"What for, my dear?"

"They give a bad impression."

The Father gathered up the three pairs of huge snowboots. He could not make head or tail of the situation. Even his little Ella had bewildered him. But he was used to doing meekly what he was told. The Stepmother covered his departure with her sweeping skirts and asked, "At what hour, sir, does His Royal Highness expect us?"

"When the coffee is cold, when the toast is stiff, when the eggshell is empty, and when the marmalade is no more—in brief, plump after breakfast." The Herald rolled up his scroll. "Time passes. I must dispatch. I have my duties. I perform them. Ladies—your servant."

"Sir!"

He bowed. They curtsied. The Footman sprang to the door. The Herald passed through it. The Trumpeter sounded a fanfare. The door closed behind them.

CHAPTER XXVI

Alas for the Things!

THE STEPMOTHER clapped her hands briskly. "Up with you, girls! Upstairs!"

"What for?" asked Arethusa.

"To squeeze your feet."

"What for?" asked Araminta.

"For a husband, ninny! Have you no eyes in your head?"

"Yes, I have," said Araminta pertly, "but I don't see—"

"You don't see, don't you? But *I* see," said the Stepmother. "I see your feet, and I see Thusy's feet, and I saw that slipper, the smallest slipper I ever set eyes on. And if one of you two don't get your great galumphing clodhoppers into it by hook or by crook, I'll know the reason why."

"But Ma, you know about my big toe," complained Arethusa.

"It's not as big as mine," boasted Araminta, who couldn't bear anybody to have anything more than she had. "I know what! I shall take my shoehorn! I can get anything on with my shoehorn."

"I know a trick worth two of that," said Arethusa. "I'm going to soap my heel."

"Up with you, up!" The Stepmother shooed them up the stairs and turned back into the kitchen. Ella was standing by the door, with her little handkerchief tied over her head. The Stepmother asked sharply, "Where are you going?"

"I'm going out," said Ella.

"Where to?"

"I'm going to the Palace."

"*You?*" The Stepmother gave a nasty laugh. "I think not."

"The Prince said everybody—like last time." Ella tugged desperately at the door to make her escape; but she wasn't quick enough.

The Stepmother caught her petticoat and dragged her back, saying, "And it's going to *be* like last time."

"All right, it is," said Ella. (Lovely last time! The thought of it gave her courage.) "I'm not afraid of you," she said, more boldly than she had ever dared to speak before.

"*You*—" said the Stepmother menacingly, "are *not*—afraid—of *me*?"

"No, I'm not."

"Slut!"

"I'm not."

"Don't you contradict me!" cried the Stepmother.

Ella answered excitedly, "I'm not your daughter."

"Indeed, indeed you're not my daughter!" She advanced on Ella as she spoke.

"I'm Father's daughter," said Ella, backing away. She darted round the table, keeping it between them as she continued to defy her enemy. "Father doesn't like you!"

"What!"

"Father doesn't like you—not really."

The Stepmother grabbed at Ella across the table and then rushed round after her; but Ella, far the nimbler, was on the other side before the Stepmother could say "Knife!" Oh, Ella's blood was up now! Nothing, *nothing* should stop her from going to the Palace to try on the slipper, her own

darling glass slipper. She had defied the Stepmother, and nothing had happened! What could the
Stepmother do to her, after all? Her Mother's miniature was safe inside her bodice, and there was no
invitation card to tear up *this* time!

But the Stepmother was looking dangerous.
"Come here!"

"I shan't."

"All right, young lady, we'll see!" The angry
woman seized the first weapon to hand; it happened
to be the Broom. She'd lay that about the girl's
shoulders in fine style. Brandishing the Broom, she
flew after Ella again—but before she could reach
her the Broom twisted in her hand and hit her in
the face. She dropped it with a cry, to clap her hand
to her cheek, and the Broom began bumping up
and down in front of her, thumping sturdily.

> "The Broom, the Broom,
> The bristly Broom
> Is kind to the girl
> Who is kind to the room."

"Thank you, thank you!" cried Ella gratefully.

"I'll give you thank you," snarled the Stepmother. "A red-hot poker will be even better." She
snatched the iron Poker from the hearth and uttered
a screech. The handle had turned red-hot as she

grasped it. "Ai! Ai! Ai!" she wailed, while the Fire flickered brightly.

> "The Fire, the Fire,
> The crackly Fire,
> Is burning to do
> What you desire."

"Thank you, oh, thank you!" cried Ella joyfully.

"Jabber, jabber, stop that jabber!" screamed the Stepmother, snatching up the rolling pin, and once more she made a dash at Ella, threatening her. "I'll jab you, young lady, I'll jab you!" But as she passed the Grandfather Clock, the pendulum swung clean out of the case and laid her flat on the floor.

> "The Clock, the Clock,
> The clickety Clock,
> Knows how to strike
> And is good for a knock."

And while Grandpa ticked and tocked, everything in the kitchen began thumping and rattling and creaking and clattering, calling to one another in their many voices:

> "The Things, the Things,
> The brotherly Things,

Help Cinderella!

HELP, HELP CINDERELLA!"

The Stepmother got on her hands and knees, glaring on all sides. So the Things were against her, were they? Ha, ha, she'd soon settle *their* little hash! She seized a pitcher of water out of the sink, and flung it onto the hearth—and the Fire died with a long hiss in a smother of smoke.

"Oh, stop!" implored Ella.

"No more red-hot pokers from *you*, I fancy!" sneered the Stepmother at the Fire. "Now for the Broom."

In a moment she had snapped it over her knee and was tearing out the bristles.

"Please!" cried Ella. "Please!"

"So much for you!" jeered the Stepmother, throwing the fragments into a corner. "And now—"

Her vindictive glance fell on the Clock. "Now to pluck the heart out of you, my fine friend!"

She wrenched the weights and chains and plucked out the pendulum.

"Grandpa!" called Ella, in agony for her best friend, but he had no voice to answer with. He had stopped ticking.

"Oh, Things, Things, Things!" whispered Ella. One after another her friends had died, and if they had not been her friends they would still be alive.

"That settles the Things," said the Stepmother. "And now to settle you."

But instead of making for Ella, she rushed round the room, bolting the windows, locking the doors, and pocketing the keys.

"You shan't stop me, you shan't—" sobbed Ella as each way of escape was sealed against her. Her spirit of defiance oozed away; she knew herself in the Stepmother's power again. When all was done, and the fireless, shuttered kitchen was as dark as night, the Stepmother raised her arm, pointing a long thin finger at the sobbing girl.

"Back!" she commanded. "Into your bunk with you!"

"You're going to lock me in my bunk?" whispered Ella.

"Back!" commanded the Stepmother.

"No, no, no!"

But it was useless. The Stepmother drove her trembling to the bunk, thrust her inside, slid the panel that shut it into the wall, and bolted it. In vain Ella beat frantically on the panel. "Let me out, oh, let me out!" she sobbed.

"Not till the Prince has chosen his bride, my girl."

The dreadful woman drew a deep breath of triumph. Now she would slip upstairs, locking the door behind her, and by the time Minty or Thusy had been chosen for the bride, perhaps that little minx would be properly tamed. But just a minute first to sit down and get her breath.

The Rocking Chair was the one Thing she hadn't broken. In a dim crack of light from a broken shutter she felt her way to where it stood with its back to her. Before she reached it, it began, very, very gently, to rock. She stared uneasily. Here she was, alone in the room, and yet—

From the upper floor she heard her daughters' shrill voices yelling, "Ma, Ma, aren't you never coming?"

"Don't wait for me, pets. Run along. I'll follow."

Who said that? She hadn't uttered a word—yet the voice was her own voice, and it came from the Rocking Chair.

"All right, don't be long!" called Thusa and Minta. "Good-by, Ma."

"Good-by, my precious pets."

Who—said—that? Who had stolen her voice?

The Stepmother was too petrified to speak above a whisper.

"Who said that?" she asked.

"Tweet-tweet!" answered the voice in the Rocking Chair.

CHAPTER XXVII

"Padlocks and Keys"

THE ROCKING CHAIR swung slowly round. The dim light showed a little figure huddled into it, the figure of an old woman who peered up at the Stepmother through the fringes of a ragged shawl. The old eyes were as bright as those of a bird, and they were fixed without blinking on the face of the frightened woman, while the Chair continued to rock gently, gently, to and fro.

The sense of fear was new to the Stepmother. Had she ever been really afraid of anything in her life? But she was now. She must turn the tables, she must make this queer little creature be afraid of *her*. Yet she couldn't quite control the tremor in her voice as she spluttered, "You old vagrant! You old tramp! Be off with you! I'll have you locked up for trespassing."

"*You'll* have *me* locked up," chuckled the old woman. "What do you think I've come for?"

"To steal, I expect," snorted the Stepmother.

"To *steal*?" The old woman chuckled again, and went on rocking softly. "On the contrary"— and now she got out of the Chair and talked in a different voice altogether—"I have come to restore your Things."

"My—?"

"The Things you have just destroyed."

The old woman began to hobble round the room, pointed her knotty crutch imperiously here and there. First at the fireplace:

> "Burn, Fire, burn!
> Luck is on the turn!
> Flame, flicker,
> Faster! quicker!
> Burn, Fire, burn!

Instantly the Fire broke into lambent flames, which lit up the queer little figure as it uttered its spells.

Next, the Broom!

"Mend, Broom, mend!
Trouble now shall end!
Besom, hustle!
Bristle, bustle!
Mend, Broom, mend!"

And the Broom bumped up and down, as whole as ever.

Now, the Grandfather Clock—

"Go, Clock, go!
Time shall conquer woe!
Daytime, nighttime,
Tell the right time!
Go, Clock, go!"

"Tick-tock! Tick-tock!" The weights pulled on the chain, the pendulum swung to and fro; Grandfather was himself again.

What next? The old woman was hobbling faster than ever, hither and thither, pointing her crutch at the windows and the doors.

"Shoot, Bolt, shoot!
Shutter follow suit!
Kitchen, brighten!
Laugh and lighten!
Shoot, Bolt, shoot!"

And although the keys were deep in the Stepmother's pocket, the doors flew open and the shutters swung away from the windows, and the morning sun filled the kitchen with light. The shadows fled away into the corners. The kitchen seemed alive with joy and laughter.

The Stepmother could now see the little figure plainly. What was there to frighten her in this tiny crooked creature bent over its crutch? But the Stepmother *was* afraid, fearfully afraid, and her fear redoubled when the old woman raised her crutch again and pointed it at the bunk in which Ella had been locked. The panel slid away—and there was nobody in it.

"Who—are—you?" whispered the Stepmother, with chattering teeth.

The crutch moved slowly through the air until it was pointing at the Stepmother. "Back!" said the old woman.

The Stepmother cowered and whimpered, "No!"

"Back!" The old woman advanced upon her as only five minutes ago she herself had advanced upon Ella.

"You're going to lock me—in—the bunk?" whimpered the Stepmother.

Driving her backward, step by step, the old woman muttered:

"Padlocks and keys,
Padlocks and keys,
What's sauce for the goslings
Is sauce for the geese.
Clink! Clank!
Clinkety-clank!
You've nobody but
Yourself to thank.
Back! Back!
Clickety-clack!
The bunk is dark
And the bunk is black.
Clonk! Clunk!
Clonkety-clunk!
Up with you, up with you,
Into the bunk!"

The Stepmother felt herself being forced backward and bundled into the bunk by a power she could not resist. The panel slid into place. She knocked on it feebly, crying, "Let me out!" But the old woman paid no more heed to her plea than she had paid to Ella's.

In fact, the old woman was no longer there. In her place stood an enchanting Fairy with butterfly wings and a star-pointed wand, and a rose wreath on her head. And in the sunlit doorway stood Ella herself, rubbing her dazzled eyes, barefoot, tangle-haired, and tattered, but with a face as fresh as a flower.

"Godmother!" She ran into the kitchen. "How did I get here?"

"Away with you!" said the Fairy. "Time is flying. Isn't that so, Grandpa?"

"That—is—so," ticked the Clock, "that—is—so."

"Grandpa, you're ticking!" Ella's eyes flew round the kitchen, brimming with joy. "Oh, Fire! Oh, Broom! Oh, Things! Oh, Grandpa, Grandpa!" She ran and hugged the Clock and kissed its face.

"To the Palace! Away!" commanded the Fairy.

"Oh yes, oh yes! But Tabby *must* have her milk." Ella snatched up the milk jug, which, instead of the usual drain of milk, brimmed over with cream. When she stooped to pour it into Tabitha's saucer in the cupboard—*there* was a lovely sight! Tabby, purring deeply over five tiny creatures, five greedy morsels, all as blind as—

"*Kittens!*" cried Ella. "Oh, oh, she's got her kittens! Oh, Tabby! Your *lovely* kittens!"

"Will you never away?" scolded the Fairy.

Ella awayed outside, into the snow. The Fairy

awayed inside, into the air. The Clock chimed the hour—the Fairy's crutch must have gone to his head, or his heart, for he went on chiming like a peal of wedding bells.

CHAPTER XXVIII

Ladies at the Gates

WHILE THE GRANDFATHER CLOCK was
striking in the kitchen, the Royal Clock was striking
in the Palace. It put the Herald in a perfect fuss.

Had he not been up and about and in and out,
hence, thence, and whence, hither and thither and
all of a dither, performing, since long before day-
break, the various, multifarious, unaccountable,
unsurmountable, unprecedented, one might almost
say the deliberately invented duties which had ac-
cumulated ever since the Prince's order to have all
the ladies back in the throne room by nine o'clock
to try on the glass slipper which the Zany had found

in the snow? Now it is one thing to be a Personage on the spot (and the Herald was fully aware that a Personage of his importance would be far-to-seek, being, so-to-speak, Unique); but another thing altogether to expect a Personage to be a hundred persons in a hundred places at one and the same moment. It was, considered as such, a touch too much.

So he flustered up and down through all the departments demanding his attention, with the Trumpeter, the Footman, and the Toastmaster flying to his call at every other minute.

He summoned them again as the clock struck. "Is everything prepared?"

The Toastmaster assured him, "Everything."

"Nothing has been overlooked?"

"Nothing," promised the Trumpeter.

"The golden footstool is ready to be placed exactly in position?"

"Exactly," asserted the Footman.

"The Army has been scrupulously mounting guard over the glass slipper?"

"Scrupulously," declared all three.

Completely unreassured, the Herald paced up and down.

"Ha! These functions! These receptions! These ceremonies! These *grandes assemblées*! One on top of the other. Helter-skelter! Holus-bolus! Scramble-jamble! I have not been to bed, I am worn to a shred, my nerves are tattered, my *esprit* is shattered, I seem to have been fated when created to be irritated, exasperated, frustrated, and prostrated! And the whole countryside is in the same condition. When I made my round this morning—like any milkman—everybody was still up; nobody had had time to sleep a wink, to change a rag, or to sponge a little finger. And now, scramble-jamble, holus-bolus, helter-skelter, back they all flock with their fate in their feet, only, mark my word, to be sent packing again with their hearts in their boots."

A doorbell clanged outside.

"There! It begins already! Ladies at the East Gate." He waved the Footman away. "Let them in."

The Footman flew to the East Gate.

Another bell clanged.

"Ladies at the West Gate." The Herald flourished a hand at the Trumpeter. "Admit them."

The Trumpeter sped to the West Gate.

Two more bells clanged.

"Ladies at the North Gate and at the South Gate." The Herald waved both hands at the Toastmaster. "Divide yourself in two, my friend, and depart, depart."

The Toastmaster did his utmost to obey.

"As for me," the Herald mused wearily, "I shall resign, abdicate, relinquish my office, and give a year's notice. Do they surge? Do they throng?" he inquired of the returning Footman.

"Like bees," said the Footman.

"Do they stream? Do they swarm?" asked the Herald of the reappearing Trumpeter.

"Like ants," he said.

"And all," said the Herald disdainfully, "all because somebody left a slipper behind at a party! People are always leaving things behind at parties— fans, bangles, muffs, puffs, gardenias, carnations, decorations, reputations— What is it *now*?" he asked of the Toastmaster peevishly, for he didn't like being interrupted in his creative and recreative moments.

The Toastmaster informed him, "A royal command."

"To what effect?"

"No shoehorns," said the Toastmaster.

"No shoehorns?" repeated the Herald.

"No shoehorns?" and "No shoehorns?" echoed the Footman and the Trumpeter.

"No shoehorns," reiterated the Toastmaster stolidly. He allowed it to sink in before he boomed, "A further royal command."

"Proceed."

"No soaped heels."

"No soaped heels?"

The Footman and the Trumpeter asked each other, "No soaped heels?"

"No soaped heels," said the Toastmaster without compromise. "A final royal command."

"Give tongue," said the Herald, as though a final royal command was his last straw.

"The Prince proclaims that, to make assurance doubly sure, it is his intention to try the glass slipper on the ladies himself."

"Himself?" Could the Herald believe his ears?

"Him—" began the Footman, but thought better of it.

The Trumpeter said, "H'm!"

"The Prince," boomed the Toastmaster, "will try the glass slipper on the ladies *himself*." And he withdrew to the congenial task of falling in love with the ladies as they presented themselves for trial.

"Himself! So be it. Authority must be obeyed, royalty must be humored. But really," said the Herald witheringly, "*himself*! I must say, it sounds more menial than hymeneal to me." And he thought, not for the first time, how strange it was that some men were born to princehood, and others were not.

And now there was a hubbub of bells clanging

incessantly at the four gates, and of chattering ladies streaming through the corridors.

"You hear them? Last night's excitement was nothing to this. Hustle!" said the Herald to the Footman. "Bustle!" he conjured the Trumpeter. "You have your duties. Perform them."

"What a morning!" said the Footman, going one way.

"What a morning!" said the Trumpeter, going the other.

"What, what a morning!" said the Herald, and retired to the throne room to superintend the disposal of the glass slipper on the gold footstool, and the sorting of the ladies all over again.

CHAPTER XXIX

"Will She, Will She Fit the Shoe?"

THE LADIES, however, were entirely unsortable. They flocked round the Herald, crying, "The slipper! The slipper! We've come for the slipper!" till he could hardly hear himself think. In vain, his hands to his ears, he pointed out to them that silence is golden, that the amorous are never clamorous, that to be loquacious is ungracious, and to be tacit is an asset—in ever-rising excitement they persisted in crying out to him that they had come for the slipper! To try on the slipper! Where was the slipper, the slipper, the slipper?—until, losing his temper once and for all, he shouted, *"Stop that noise!"*

The ladies stopped instantly; and this, oddly enough, offended him to the extreme. His courtesy had been wasted on them. They had obliged him to resort to Bad Manners. Where, he asked himself, had these ladies been brought up?

In very ill humor he proceeded up the room to the throne, where the Prince was awaiting him. The glass slipper had already been placed on the gold footstool in front of the trying-on chair—and not too well placed, decided the Herald. He bent down, readjusted it with the slightest of touches, and addressed himself to the Prince.

"Your Royal Highness is ready for action?"

"I am."

"The arrangements are to your satisfaction?"

"They are."

"We may proceed according to instructions?"

"You may."

"And it is for me to make the introductions?"

"It is."

"So be it! Trumpeter!"

The Trumpeter sounded a fanfare. The ladies pressed forward.

The Prince was somewhat appalled by their numbers; it looked as though his task would be never-ending. He had proclaimed his intention of trying on the slipper himself, because he could not endure the thought of anybody else so much as touching the tiny foot of the Princess of Nowhere when she made her appearance. And suppose, as he hoped, she should come in first of all, his task would be finished in the twinkling of an eye.

But alas! She did not come in first—or second, or third. As each pretty girl advanced gladly, the Prince's heart missed a beat—if the slipper should fit her, his royal word was pledged. And as each foot failed, and its owner retired sadly, the Prince heaved a little sigh of relief that only the Zany heard—and the Zany heaved an enormous sigh that could be heard by everybody. The Herald conducted the applicants to and from the chair; and the Toastmaster stood by, ready to chant the praises of the bride.

At last there were only six ladies left. When the Herald led the first of these to the kneeling Prince and announced, "Her Transcendency the Baroness of Allspice!" the Toastmaster could contain himself no longer, and burst irrepressibly into song.

"Allspice, all hail! All hail, Allspice!
  So tall, so trim, so neat, so nice!
  Whose charms are rare, whose faults are few—"

"But will she," asked the Herald, "will she fit the shoe?"

The ladies craned forward. Her Transcendency really had a very small foot. The Prince's hand trembled as he tried the slipper on.

No! Yes! No! *No, no, no, no, no!* The ladies who had already been found wanting whispered among themselves, "No wedding bells, no cake, no rice, no, nothing at all for tall Allspice!"

Sorrowfully but gracefully the Baroness retired. Her Supremacy the Countess of Caraway replaced her on the gilt trying-on chair. The Toastmaster's soft heart spilled over once more.

"Sing Caraway! O Caraway!
No bud more blithe! No bloom more gay!
No breeze more coy or sweet to woo—"

"But will she, will she fit the shoe?" inquired the Herald.

"No!" whispered half the ladies. "Yes!" whispered the other half. "No, no, no, no, no!" they whispered all together. "No bliss, no joy, no glee today, no, nothing at all for Caraway!"

"Her Arrogance the Viscountess of Cloves!"

"Now cleave the air," caroled the Toastmaster.

"Now cleave the air in praise of Cloves!
   Not Venus' doves in Attic groves
   More gently bill! More sweetly coo!"

"But," doubted the Herald, "will she, *will* she fit the shoe?"

No—yes—no— "No, no, no, no, no!" whispered the ladies. "Fair Venuses were made for Joves, but nothing at all was made for Cloves."

Her Magnificence the Marquise of Cinnamon came next, and the Toastmaster oozed his adoration.

"More bright Apollo never shone
   Than shine the eyes of Cinnamon!
   No pool more clear! No sky more blue—"

"But will she, will she," demanded the Herald, "fit the shoe?"

No! Yes! No! "No, no, no, no, no!" The ladies, heads together, whispered happily, "With one shoe off and one shoe on, no, nothing at all for Cinnamon."

Would Her Exuberance the Margravine of Mace fare better? The Toastmaster made gooseberry eyes at her as she sat down and presented to the Prince her elegant silk-stockinged foot.

"The stately Margravine of Mace
  Exceeds the Graces three in grace!
  Her foot is firm! Her step is true—"

"But will she, will she fit," objected the Herald, "the shoe?"

No, she would not! The ladies clapped their hands. No—yes—no! "No, no, no, no, no! No palm, no prize, no pride of place, no Prince, no nothing at all for Mace."

The Prince sighed thankfully, though his heart was sore. Here came the last of them, Her Pomposity the Archduchess of Cochineal. Fate could not be so cruel as to supply her with the tiniest of feet. She seated herself with such ease and distinction that the Toastmaster was inspired to inquire:

"What polish! style! and what appeal
  Can equal that of Cochineal?
  What birth!
  What breeding through and through—"

But the Herald merely asked himself, Would she, or wouldn't she, fit the shoe? Polish, style, appeal, birth, breeding—what were all these if the Archducal foot was too long or too wide? No! Yes! No! "No, no, no, no, no!" rejoiced the ladies.

"No joyful chime, no cheerful peal, no, nothing at all for Cochineal. Nothing for me, and nothing for you! No foot at all to fit the shoe."

The Prince rose to his feet. So *that* was over.

But hark! There was a scurry and a hurry and a flurry at the door, and in burst Araminta and Arethusa, who had raced all the way from home and arrived neck and neck. They were both out of breath as they gasped, "Are we late, are we late? It isn't over, is it?"

"Is *what* not over?" said the Herald icily. "Is not *what* over? *What* is not over?"

"The shoe!" they answered together. "We've come to try on the shoe."

The Prince looked at them with dismay. "*Must* they?" he asked quietly.

"Your Royal Highness's Proclamation said everybody," the Herald reminded him.

"But are there not limits—?"

The Herald shrugged. "A proclamation is a proclamation. A pronunciamento is a pronunciamento."

"Very well. Try on the slipper."

"*I!*" The Herald drew himself up. "Your Royal Highness's Proclamation declared explicitly that Your Royal Highness would *himself*—"

He disdained to finish, but implied very plainly

that if royalty *would* make rules, royalty must observe them. The Prince returned unwillingly to the footstool and knelt before Araminta, who had ensconced herself in the gilt seat after playing a sort of musical chairs for it with Arethusa. She had got there by sheer pushing.

"MISS ARAMINTA!" announced the Herald.

The Toastmaster swallowed hard and trolled forth:

> "Is not a scarecrow with a squint a
> Sweeter sight than Araminta?
> Close the eyes! Avert the view—"

"Oh, will she, will she fit the shoe?" shuddered the Herald.

All closed their eyes and averted their views— and Araminta seized her chance to whip out her shoehorn and get to work. She tugged and she tussled, and tussled and tugged in vain. Suddenly one of the ladies, whose view was not sufficiently averted, cried, "A cheat! A cheat! She's using a shoehorn!"

"Leave the chair!" commanded the Herald in freezing tones.

"For cheats and frauds and tricks unfair, there's nothing at all, so leave the chair!" chimed the ladies.

Araminta got up, blushing with confusion. Delighted with her sister's downfall, Arethusa shoved past her, putting out her tongue, scrambled into the chair, and beamed expectantly at the Herald. There was nothing for it but to announce, "MISS ARETHUSA!" which he did in a very loud voice with a very bad grace.

The Toastmaster did his best to make the worst of it.

> "The gorgon features of Medusa
> Comelier were than Arethusa
> What is nature coming to?"

"Can she, oh *can* she fit the shoe?" The Herald paled at the thought.

Arethusa was stooping very low and fumbling in a curious manner under her dress. Supposing that her stocking was coming down, the Prince, with great delicacy, turned his head away. But the ladies, without any delicacy at all, craned forward to see what she was up to.

"A swindle! A swindle!" they cried. "She's soaping her heel."

"Vacate your seat!" commanded the Herald, in tones that would have blighted a rhinoceros, while the ladies, as one woman, insisted, "For chits in chairs who choose to cheat, there's nothing at all, so leave your seat."

Arethusa left her seat, wishing she hadn't come.

"Thank heaven for that," breathed the Prince. The Zany fell upon his knees and thanked heaven. "But where," cried the Prince, "where is my Princess?" The Zany looked up at the ceiling, and down at the floor, and felt in both his pockets. The Princess of Nowhere wasn't anywhere, and the Zany, in his grief, heaved a sigh so heavy that the curtains began to wave wildly all round the room.

The Herald observed, "There's a wind rising."

"A monsoon!" said the Footman. The ladies were clutching their skirts to hold them down.

"A simoon!" declared the Trumpeter. The chandeliers were chattering like teeth.

"A typhoon!" boomed the Toastmaster, for now everything and everybody in the room was billowing and bellowing and swirling and whirling, and curling and unfurling, and rotating and gyrating and circulating, and in short, thought the Herald, circumnavigating as though Chaos were come again, and the universe were in a process of re-creation.

Which, in a sort of a way, was just what *was* happening.

CHAPTER XXX

The Hand of Cinderella

THE WIND stopped blowing, the curtains stopped flowing, the Zany stopped spinning like a teetotum, the ladies stopped running round in circles and began to smooth their ruffled curls and straighten their ruffled furbelows. The throne room looked just as it did before the hullabaloo.

But did it? In the middle of the floor was a little old woman who had certainly not been there before, a Crone in a ragged shawl crouched over a crutch; and, in a strange way that nobody could explain, her presence seemed to make a great deal

of difference. Where had she come from, and how
had she got there?

While everybody was thinking these questions,
the Prince was asking them.

"Who are you? What have you come for? Where
have you come from? What is your name?"

The Crone wagged her head and chuckled.

> "What is my name?
> What is my name?
> I'm only a hob–hob–
> hobbledy dame.
> Who be I?
> Lack-a-day-dee!
> Nobody, nobody,
> That's who I be.
> Why do I come
> With crutch in hand?
> I come for nothing
> You'd understand.
> Whence do I come
> In tattery shawl?
> I come from nowhere
> At all, at all."

"From Nowhere?" cried the Prince.

"At all, at all," said she.

"You come from Nowhere?"

"What I say once is true."

"You know the Princess of Nowhere?"

"Which princess?" asked she.

"There can be but one," said the Prince.

"Hoity-toity!" She chuckled. "Nowhere is chock-a-block with princesses."

"Mine," said the Prince, "is the most beautiful."

"Beauty," said the Crone, "is a matter of opinion. What is she like?"

"Her eyes are like stars, her teeth are like pearls, her hair is like silk, her skin is like milk. Her mouth is like a rose."

The old woman said, "All princesses are like stars, pearls, silk, milk, and roses. How was she dressed?"

"As the fairest princess in the world should be dressed," said the Prince.

"H'm," said the Crone. "That's a pity."

"Why?"

"The only princess in my pocket is in rags," said the Crone.

"No better than our Cinders!" exclaimed Arethusa.

"My princess had glass slippers on her feet," said the Prince.

"My princess goes barefoot," said the Crone.

"Just like our Cinders!" exclaimed Araminta.

The Prince asked impatiently, "What are you talking of? Who is this Cinders?"

The Herald deigned to explain. "Their Stepsister, I presume—Miss Ella."

"Ella? What Ella?" The Prince looked round the room. "Why isn't she here?"

"Her!" cried Arethusa.

"Here?" cried Araminta.

"My Royal Proclamation said everybody," cried the Prince.

"But she's a slavey," said Arethusa.

"Everybody."

"But she's a nobody," said Araminta.

The Crone remarked, "The Princess of Nowhere should be a Nobody."

The Prince turned to her quickly. "You are wise, old woman." He clasped his hands. "Help me!"

"Tweet-tweet!" chirped she.

And now something more surprising than the windstorm filled the room—it was filled with the fluttering of thousands of wings, and the chirpings and twitterings from thousands of tiny throats; the light grew dark with feathers, and for a few moments nobody could see anything. Then the twittering ceased, the wings flew away—and there, in the gilt chair, sat Ella herself, Ella in her rags and tangled hair, with one little bare foot on the gold stool; and the Prince was kneeling before her. He looked up at her, and she down on him, with joy and wonder.

"Am I really here?" she asked.

"You are really here."

"Is this really me?"

"It is really you."

"And is that really you?" She bent down closer and asked him, "I'm not dreaming?"

"Your eyes are wide, wide awake," he promised her; and she said, "Put on the slipper."

He put the slipper on. "It fits!" he cried.

"And here is its mate," said Ella, drawing the other slipper out of her skirt.

He put on that one too, and the whole Court shouted, "It fits!"

Ella wanted but one thing more to complete her great happiness. The Prince knew it, without knowing what it was. "What do you want?" he asked.

Ella whispered shyly, "Will you—kiss my hand?"

The Prince took Ella's grubby little hand, still

dirty with the morning's cinders, and kissed it as tenderly as if it had been the white hand of the Princess of Nowhere. Then he sprang to his feet and cried in a ringing voice, "Let all present kiss the hand of Cinderella!"

The Herald marshaled the ladies into place, and conducted them, one after the other, to the dais where Ella was standing beside the Prince; and, one after the other, each kissed her hand, curtsied deeply, and passed on. Meanwhile the Toastmaster, his heart melted once and for all, sang his song for the bride.

"Blue eyes, yellow hair,
Our Queen is fair.

Little hands, tiny feet,
She is sweet.

Sun, shine! Birds, be gay
For her today.

Life give her joy, love give her flowers,
This Queen of ours."

"Life, give her joy! Love, give her flowers!" sang the ladies. They did not grudge her her good fortune; how could anyone not love someone who looked so like a flower?

Yes, how could anyone—even Arethusa and Araminta? They came slowly at the end of the procession, approaching the dais last of all, with hanging heads and faces burning with shame. Then their courage failed them; they dared not come farther, and stopped halfway, with their eyes fixed on the ground. Now they were going to get their deserts for all their unkindness.

And Ella from the dais looked at them, the Sisters who had been so cruel and harsh and greedy and thoughtless—thoughtless! Perhaps, perhaps that was all it was, just thoughtlessness. She was so happy—and everything must be lovely when everything is lovely!

She jumped down from the dais and ran to the Sisters. "Thusy!" She kissed Arethusa on the right cheek. "Minty!" She kissed Araminta on the left, and ran back to the Prince.

The Sisters lifted their heads a little and stared at each other. Could they believe it? They had been kissed by a Princess! Nobody noticed them as they stole away home.

On the dais the Prince had taken Ella's hands in his and was saying, "I wish—I wish—"

"What do you wish?" asked the old Crone, whom everybody had completely forgotten.

"Do you wish for the Kingdom of Nowhere,
Where to dream is the same as to do?

Do you wish to be happy forever, and go where
Your wishes come true?"

"Please, old woman," said the Prince.
"Please, Granny," said Ella.
The Crone tossed her crutch in the air.

"Zany, Zany, witless and wise,
Show your Prince where Nowhere lies—"

As the Zany caught the crutch it changed in
his hand to a rod of silver light, tipped with a star.
Gleeful as a child let loose among its fancies, he
began to spin round and round the room like a top,
humming as he spun, slapping his wand on the
floor, on the walls, on the ceiling, to which he
floated up like a balloon. Wherever the wand pointed,
and whatever it touched, changed into something
different: the Crone took wings like a bird, the
Toastmaster tumbled about like a clown, the Footman tripped over him like a pantaloon, the Trumpeter became an Oriental magician dispensing charms
and spells, the Herald a slashing, dashing Spanish
buccaneer, an all-conquering Don Juan. The ladies
turned into butterflies, the lords into dragonflies,
the Palace into a comet which flew with them all
three times round the sun, where the Prince, looking very like a Harlequin, found the rosy heart that

had flown away at the ball, and presented it to Ella, looking very like a Columbine, who clutched it so tight that it couldn't ever fly away again. . . .

The Zany was spinning slower, the humming was lower, the top was running down. . . .

The magic ended all in an instant, as it had begun. Ladies and lords were themselves again, Herald and Toastmaster, Footman and Trumpeter, resumed their own shapes and went on performing their duties. The Zany was exactly what he had always been. The Crone had vanished, and the Palace had come back to earth.

Only Ella and the Prince had left a part of themselves in Nowhere, where wishes come true.